HUGHLINGS JACKSON ON PSYCHIATRY

A

HUGHLINGS JACKSON ON PSYCHIATRY

by

KENNETH DEWHURST
T.D., M.D., D. Phil., F.R.C. Psych., D.P.M.
Professor of Psychiatry, University of the West Indies
Kingston, Jamaica

SANDFORD PUBLICATIONS, OXFORD 1982

Price £9.00

© Kenneth Dewhurst 1982
ISBN 0 9501528 6 2

Typeset by Illustration Services, Oxford
Printed in Great Britain by Tempest Printing, Oxford

Contents

Introduction

Jacksonian neurodynamic principles influenced Sigmund Freud, and with various modifications were re-applied in psychiatry, notably by Henri Ey in France, Jan Mazurkiewicz in Poland, and Adolf Meyer in the United States. Some Jacksonian principles are still relevant, and it is hoped that this review will make them better known.

Several of Hughlings Jackson's most significant writings first appeared in a variety of medical journals including some rather obscure ones such as the *West Riding Lunatic Asylum Medical Reports*, and the *Transactions of the St. Andrews Medical Graduates Association*, neither of them being readily available even in major centres. Hughlings Jackson's modesty was such that he could never be persuaded to write a book, but James Taylor edited a collection of his later writings as *The Neurological Fragments of J. Hughlings Jackson, with a Biographical Memoir* (1925) which has long been out of print. With the assistance of F. M. R. Walshe and Gordon Holmes, James Taylor also edited a wider selection of Jackson's writings in two volumes entitled: *Selected Writings of John Hughlings Jackson* (1931/2). The first volume contains his major contributions on epilepsy while the second is a collection of papers on speech disorders, evolution and dissolution in the nervous system, together with miscellaneous essays and addresses on neurology and neuropsychiatry. Reprinted in

1958, *Selected Writings* is now difficult to obtain. The demand for Jackson's writings reflects, not only current interest in his outstanding contributions to neurology, but also his ideas on aspects of neuropsychiatry.

In this book I have drawn on all the sources of Hughlings Jackson's writings on neuropsychiatry (including those on temporal lobe epilepsy) many of which were not included in Taylor's edition. And whenever appropriate I have given a cross reference in brackets to the volume and page number in *Selected Writings*.

Hughlings Jackson's strict neurological attitude to psychiatry is the main reason for the limitation of his ideas. There is, however, increasing evidence indicating that the major psychoses, like neurological diseases, may be manifestations of brain disorders, and hence Jacksonian principles may profitably be applied to them. But Jackson's approach to the psychoneuroses was somewhat dismissive as is apparent in his statement that "if there be such a thing as a disease of the mind, we can do nothing for it".

Since Hughlings Jackson's time, the psychological and sociological aspects of psychiatry have become established, although these disciplines also have their limitations. It would be particularly gratifying, for example, if such laudable feats of social engineering as the abolition of Victorian asylums, and the vigorous eradication of slum dwellings, were able to contribute significantly to the relief of the major psychoses. A too optimistic belief in the beneficial effects of environmental influences has found expression in Russell Barton's *Institutional Neurosis* (1959). Here Barton ascribes apathy, loss of initiative, submissiveness, lack of individuality, the maintenance of an awkward and dejected posture together with the characteristic gait seen in some chronic psychiatric hospital patients to "institutionalisation". But photographs of these patients reveal the typical volitional defects of chronic schizophrenia, a late manifestation in the natural history of that disease. In any event, it is not a 'neurosis' but a common feature seen in a chronic psychosis. Further, others living in institutions such as the armed services, public schools, prisons, colleges and universities do not appear to develop a similar syndrome.

As an eccentric Victorian and hard-headed Yorkshireman, Hughlings Jackson's attitude to psychiatry was entirely opposite to that of the environmentalist: he regarded neuropsychiatry as part of neurology and subject to the same discipline as other branches of medicine.

Acknowledgements

I am most grateful to Dr. B. Alapin, who first mentioned the writings of Jan Mazurkiewicz; and to Dr. Philip Evans for stimulating my interest in Henri Ey's organo-dynamic psychiatry. I should also like to thank Dr. M. R. Trimble for drawing my attention to the excellent paper by Taylor and Marsh on 'Dr. Z'; and to Dr. William Feindel, Director of the Montreal Neurological Institute, for information on the Hughlings Jackson Memorial Lectures.

From the Department of Psychiatry of the University of the West Indies I am most grateful for the advice of Dr. Frank Knight, senior lecturer and head of department, and for the secretarial assistance of Rita Robertson and Bernadette Pierre.

I am also grateful to Mr. Ivor Levy, F.R.C.S. and Audrey Beecham for reading the typescript and suggesting improvements. In particular I would like to thank my friend Dr. John Todd for his meticulous revision of the typescript; for eliminating several errors and considerably improving the text. I am also obliged to Leofranc Holford-Strevens for preparing the index and supervising it through the press.

For secretarial assistance I am obliged to Edith Quinn, Margaret Matheson, and Frieda Houser; I would also like to thank Clare Gibbs and Mike Humphries of "Illustration Services" for rapidly preparing the proofs. In particular I am most grateful to Anna Kovac for her constant encouragement and support.

20 February 1981   *Kingston, Jamaica*

John Hughlings Jackson (1835–1911): Chronological Outline of his Career

1835	Born 4th April, Providence Green, Green Hammerton, near Knaresborough, Yorkshire.
c. 1840–1850	Attended schools at Green Hammerton, Tadcaster, and Nailsworth, Gloucestershire.
1850–1855	Apprentice to Dr. William Charles Anderson at 23 Stonegate, York and medical student at York Hospital Medical School.
1855	Short period at St. Bartholomew's Hospital, London, where Sir James Paget (1814–99) was one of his teachers.
1856	Qualified L.S.A. (Licentiate of the Society of Apothecaries) and M.R.C.S. (Member of the Royal College of Surgeons).
1856–1859	House physician at the York Dispensary.
1859–1861	Moved to London and resided with Jonathan Hutchinson (1828–1913) at 14 Finsbury Circus.
1859	Lecturer in pathology, morbid anatomy, and histology at the London Hospital Medical School. Assistant physician to Metropolitan Free Hospital and to Islington Dispensary. Reporter, *Medical Times and Gazette*.

1860	M.D., St. Andrew's University, clinical assistant to Mr. Alfred Poland, Moorfields Eye Hospital.
1861	Moved to 4 Finsbury Circus. M.R.C.P. (Member of the Royal College of Physicians).
1862	Assistant physician to the National Hospital for the Paralysed and Epileptic, Queen Square. Worked with Charles-Édouard Brown-Séquard (1817–94) for about one year.
1863	Assistant physician to the London Hospital and lecturer in physiology. Privately published a fifty-page pamphlet entitled: *Suggestions for studying Diseases of the Nervous System on Professor Owen's Vertebral Theory*.
1864	Published "Clinical remarks on hemiplegia with valvular disease of the heart" on the basis of 28 cases of loss of speech with right hemiplegia. On 21st May 1864 wrote in the *B.M.J.*: "M. Broca believes that disease of the brain on the left side only produces loss of speech, and . . . if I were to judge from the cases under my care, I should think so too . . ." He went on to acknowledge that "on every point of importance I have been anticipated by M. Broca". Interested in the writings of the associationist psychologists George Henry Lewes (1817–78), Alexander Bain (1819–1903), and particularly Herbert Spencer (1819–1903), whose evolutionary theories he began to apply in neurology.
1865	Married his cousin Elizabeth Dade Jackson and moved to 28 Bedford Place.

1866	Joined Medico-Psychological Association.
1867	Appointed physician to the National Hospital, Queen Square. Moved to 3 Manchester Square.
1868	Debated problems of aphasia with Paul Broca at the Congress of the British Association for the Advancement of Science, Norwich. Elected F.R.C.P. (Fellow of the Royal College of Physicians).
1869	Goulstonian Lecturer, Royal College of Physicians. "Certain Points of Study and Classification of Diseases of the Nervous System".
1870	Published "A study of convulsions," *Trans. St. Ands. Med. Grad. Assoc.* **3**, p. 162, summarised *Lancet* **2**, p. 674 (1870), *Amer. J. of Med. Sci.* **61**, pp. 229–31 (1871). Published as a forty-five-page pamphlet by Adell and Ives, London 1870. Trans. O. Sittig, *J. Hughlings Jackson's Eine Studie über Krämpfe*. He discussed unilateral convulsions and anticipated the experimental findings of Fritsch and Hitzig.
1872	Hunterian Oration, "On physiological aspects of Education", *B.M.J.* **1**, p. 179.
1874	Physician to the London Hospital.
1876	25th May, Mrs. Jackson died, aged 39.
1877	Annual Oration to the Medical Society of London on "Ophthalmology in relation to general medicine" (*Lancet*, 1st May 1877).
1878	Elected F.R.S. (Fellow of the Royal Society). One of the joint founder-editors of *Brain*.
1879	Harveian lectures, "On the Diagnosis of Epilepsy".

1884	Croonian Lecturer, Royal College of Physicians. "On Evolution and dissolution of the nervous system".
1885	Bowman Lecturer to Ophthalmological Society, "Ophthalmology and Diseases of the Nervous System". Member of Council of Royal College of Physicians (1885–7).
1886	First President of the Neurological Society of London.
1888–1890	Censor of the Royal College of Physicians of London.
1889	Addressed the Leeds meeting of the B.M.A. on "Comparative Study of Diseases of the Nervous System".
1890	Lumleian Lecturer, Royal College of Physicians on "Convulsive Seizures", a summary of his work.
1894	Retired from staff of the London Hospital. Presentation made by Sir James Paget, who mentioned Jackson's fruitful researches into the localisation of brain function, which had "given lucidity to physiology and guidance to surgery".
1897	8th December gave the first Hughlings Jackson lecture on "Remarks on the relations of different divisions of the central nervous system to one another and to other parts of the body". *Lancet* (1898) 1, p. 79, *B.M.J.* (1898) 1, p. 65.
1898	Introduced S. Weir Mitchell to Herbert Spencer.
1901	Urged by Sir William Osler, Weir Mitchell, and James Putnam to publish a book based on his main contributions to neurology.

1903 Awarded Moxon Gold Medal, Royal College of Physicians. Other honours included LL.D. from Universities of Glasgow and Edinburgh, D.Sc., University of Leeds, M.D., Bologna. Honorary Fellowship of the Royal College of Physicians in Ireland and corresponding member of the Royal Academy of Medicine of Belgium.

1904 Elected honorary member of the Neurology Society of London.

1906 Retired from the active staff of the National Hospital, Queen Square. Neurological Society dedicated to him Part IV of *Brain* "as a tribute of Respect and Affection, in the 50th year of his Medical Practice".

1907 His marble bust, subscribed by medical and surgical colleagues at the National Hospital, was presented by Sir William Gowers on 21st November.

1911 Died on 7th October and buried at Highgate Cemetery.

Psychiatric Background

Hughlings Jackson began his medical career as an apprentice to a general practitioner in York, where he attended the Medical School. Here he was introduced to psychiatry and neuropsychiatry by Daniel Hack Tuke (1827–95) and Thomas Laycock (1812–76) respectively. Tuke lectured on psychological medicine at the Medical School, and also treated psychiatric outpatients at the Public Dispensary. He was visiting physician to 'The Retreat', founded by his great-grandfather, where he had worked as hospital steward before beginning his medical studies at St Bartholomew's Hospital. Tuke qualified M.R.C.S. in 1852, and after a year in Germany graduated M.D. at Heidelberg in 1853. He then wrote a critical survey of psychiatric care in Holland, and in 1854 won a prize for an essay on therapeutic improvements in psychiatry since Pinel. He would, therefore, have been an able, energetic and humane psychiatrist. His colleague at the Dispensary, and lecturer in clinical medicine at the Medical School, Thomas Laycock, with whom Tuke shared a broad medical background, was no less active in the fields of medicine and neuropsychiatry. After serving an apprenticeship, while attending University College London, Laycock moved to Paris, where, for two years, he studied under Lisfranc (1790–1847), Velpeau (1795–1867), and Louis (1787–1872), and on his return qualified M.R.C.S. He then went to

Germany and graduated M.D. *summa cum laude* at Göttingen in 1839. Laycock's wide reading of German medical literature was reflected in his interest in reflexology and aspects of consciousness in his translation for the Sydenham Society of the works of J. A. Unzer (1727–99) and Georg Prochaska (1749–1820). He was the first to apply Marshall Hall's (1790–1857) doctrine of reflex action to the brain, and in his *Treatise on the Nervous Diseases of Women* (1840) observed that "the organ of consciousness, is subject to the laws of reflex action, and in this respect, does not differ from other ganglia of the nervous system". At a meeting of the British Association for the Advancement of Science in 1844 Laycock elaborated on this theme in his address "On the Reflex Functions of the Brain", in which his psychiatric interests are apparent. "Insanity and dreaming present the best field for investigating the laws of that extension of action from one portion of the brain to the other", he stated, "by which ideas follow each other in sequence. An interesting example of study is now in the Retreat near York. This person seems utterly will-less. He expresses the ideas as they spontaneously arise in associated sequence, the combinations being singularly varied, but traceable to a common root, or centre of impulse. Researches of this kind, whether instituted on the insane, the somnambulist, the dreamer, or the delirious, must be considered like researches in analytical chemistry. The reagent is the impression made on the brain; the molecular changes following the application of the reagent are made known to us as ideas. In chemical analysis we know the molecular changes only by the change in form, refractive powers, and other circumstances, induced by the reagent; in cerebral analysis we *feel* the change, or observe its results on the efferent nerves." Laycock's writings show that his interest in psychiatry was much greater than was usual for a physician and a lecturer in chemical medicine. Probably accompanied by medical students, he regularly visited patients in the York psychiatric hospitals in order to find evidence in support of his belief that psychotic states were manifestations of brain disease. "Amongst the insane, especially the idiotic and fatuous", he wrote, "examples of combined excito-motory movements of cerebral origin, are not infrequent. A male patient in the York County Asylum, aged 44, and fatuous for thirty-seven years, cannot pronounce any word distinctly, nor understand what is said to him. He constantly holds a stone, or other substance, in the palm of one hand, and moves continually, as if slowly waltzing. Mr. Alderson, the resident medical officer, kindly assisted me to time his movements, and we found that he performed twenty steps in fourteen and a half or fifteen seconds, with the greatest regularity, and we measured his steps repeatedly. Another man, aged 34, in a state of dementia, stands for hours together, moving his hands and feet synchronously, in a way not easily to be described. He was found, when timed, to make twenty steps in ten and a half or eleven seconds, with unvarying regularity. In these examples, as in the case of chorea, the cause of the movements was centric; and, as the latter were connected with an idea of time, its seat was undoubtedly cerebral".

Thomas Laycock's ideas have been stressed as many of them were adopted and extended by Hughlings Jackson. Their relationship was noted by Edwin Bramwell (1935), who, after discussing other teachers including Jonathan Hutchinson (1828–1913), Sir James Paget (1814–99), and Charles-Édouard Brown-Séquard (1817–94), concluded that Laycock had the most enduring influence of them all as "the mental outlook of the two men was so similar . . .". Hughlings Jackson was taught clinical medicine by Laycock for about one year, probably between 1854 and 1855, when the latter was appointed Professor of the Practice of Physic at Edinburgh; in the same year, Jackson rounded off his studies at St. Bartholomew's Hospital before qualifying in the spring of 1856. Thus the enduring effects of Laycock's teaching reflect creditably on the standard at York. In his detailed history of the York Medical School, Wetherill (1961) estimates that there were only about a dozen medical students in Jackson's year, so that they virtually received private tuition, and were probably on more friendly and informal terms with their teachers than were others attending larger medical schools.

After qualifying, Hughlings Jackson returned to York as house physician to the Dispensary, where, among other patients, he examined those with psychiatric illnesses under Tuke's supervision. While he was working at the Dispensary, J. C. Bucknill (1817–97) and D. Hack Tuke published *A Manual of Psychological Medicine* (1858), which became the standard textbook for several decades. Bucknill and Tuke divided mental disorders into the five main groups of idiocy, dementia, delusional insanity, emotional insanity, and mania, and then subdivided each group into more specific conditions. Emotional insanity, for example, included patients with melancholia without delusions, those with mania and extravagant conduct or 'moral insanity', and others with a predisposition to homicide, suicide, or theft. Throughout his career Hughlings Jackson completely ignored psychiatric nosology, and was undoubtedly more interested in the fact that Bucknill and Tuke estimated that 6% of the chronic asylum population of epileptics were regarded as 'insane'. Jackson did, however, keep abreast of progress in psychiatry. He read subsequent editions of Bucknill and Tuke, and in 1875 referred approvingly to Anstie's concept of an "insane diathesis". In later years Jackson was on intimate terms with Bucknill and Tuke. When *Brain* was founded, in 1878, Hughlings Jackson and Sir John Bucknill were among the editorial quartet, and he renewed his friendship with Hack Tuke in 1875 when the latter moved to London.

As York was a centre for the treatment of mental disorders, Hughlings Jackson probably gained more clinical experience than most of his contemporaries in other medical schools. As well as seeing psychiatric out-patients, he occasionally accompanied Hack Tuke to the Retreat; and Greenblatt (1965) has shown that he also attended Dr. Charles Simpson's ward rounds at the York County Asylum. Jackson was friendly with another asylum doctor, Samuel North, surgeon to Dunnington House Asylum in Castlegate, who proposed him for membership of the York Medical Society, and in 1859 rendered him a greater service through his introductory letter to a former York medical student, Jonathan Hutchinson, then becoming established in London. Jackson was warmly received at his Finbury Circle home, where he stayed for two years, benefiting from the social professional, and intellectual companionship of his host. They jointly reported lectures, clinical demonstrations, and the proceedings of various medical societies for the *Medical Times and Gazette*; and it was to Hutchinson that Jackson was indebted for at least three of his earliest appointments: as lecturer in pathology at the London Hospital Medical School, assistant physician to the Metropolitan Hospital, and to the Islington Dispensary.

But a year after his arrival in London, Hughlings Jackson felt unsettled, and according to Hutchinson (1911), thought of exchanging medicine for 'philosophy'. This coincided with the publication of Thomas Laycock's *Mind and Brain: or, the Correlation of Consciousness and Organisation, with their Application to Philosophy, Zoology, Physiology, Mental Pathology, and the Practice of Medicine* (1860). It is now suggested that by 'philosophy' Hutchinson meant to include that vague hinterland between philosophy, emergent psychology, and psychiatry, which was discussed by Laycock using such terms as 'neuro-metaphysical studies', 'physiological metaphysics', and 'mental philosophy'. Such expressions would now be translated into psychology, abnormal psychology, or neuro-psychiatry, and hence it is argued that Hutchinson used 'philosophy' in a rather broader sense than is now adopted. This opinion is supported by Hughlings Jackson's many references to the works of the associationist psychologists, who were then often referred to as 'philosophers'.

In the first volume of *Mind and Brain*, Laycock tried to forge a link between 'mental philosophy' and 'cerebral physiology'; he also attempted to unravel the pathology and treatment of insanity, and investigate the relationship between psychiatric disorders and 'vice'. He claimed that "a science of human nature in its most comprehensive meaning" may only be fully understood in terms of a knowledge of brain physiology and body–mind relationships. In the second volume he stated that reflex action in the brain may take place independently of conscious awareness, and formulated his so-called "law of unconscious functional activity of the brain as the organ of consciousness". Hunter and Macalpine (1963) have pointed out that W. B. Carpenter (1813–85) in the fourth and fifth editions of his *Principles of Human Physiology* (1842–55), linked Laycock's doctrine of reflex activity of the brain with the automatic activities of mind to form the unitary concept of 'unconscious cerebration': an expression used by Hughlings Jackson to explain the rapid flow of his own ideas to his last house physician, S. A. Kinnier Wilson (1878–1937).

Although Hughlings Jackson was indebted to Hutchinson for his earliest London appointments, and for persuading him to continue in his medical career, it was Brown-Séquard who directed his interest to neurology in 1862 on Jackson's appointment as assistant physician to the National Hospital for the Paralysed and Epileptic, Queen Square. Brown-Séquard considered that it would be "foolish to waste his efforts in the wider observation of disease in general" and recommended that if he wished to "attain anything he must keep to the nervous system".

In his earliest investigations, beginning in 1864, into the association between right hemiplegia and speech disorders, Jackson's writings show that he was well acquainted with the works of the associationist psychologists such as George Henry Lewes (1817–78), Alexander Bain (1819–1903), and particularly Herbert Spencer (1819–1903), whose evolutionary doctrine he now began to apply to clinical problems. Thus, through their influence, Jackson evolved a mechanistic psycho-physiological approach to diseases of the central nervous system, which he regarded as a series of sensori-motor units developed within the evolutionary scale. Disease, he thought, was a flaw, or dissolution, in the evolutionary scheme causing negative symptoms such as a defect of consciousness. Loss of control by the highest centres unleashes from the lower intact layers such positive symptoms as delusions, hallucinations, and extravagant behaviour. In evolving this hypothesis Hughlings Jackson went out of his way to acknowledge the contributions of others, including F. E. Anstie (1833–74) and Henry Monro (1817–91). In *Remarks on Insanity: its Nature and Treatment* (1850) Monro postulated that "depressive vitality" of the "cerebral masses" caused loss of equilibrium with "partial paralysis" of one part of the brain and "irritable excess of action" of other parts. Hunter and Macalpine (1963) have traced Monro's ideas back to William Cullen (1716–90), who suggested that in mental illnesses different parts of the brain were in unequal states of 'depression' or 'excitement'. Hughlings Jackson cited Anstie's *Stimulants and Narcotics* (1864), with the first description of the principle of over-activity of lower centres as a consequence of loss of control by higher ones (I. 123n). Finally, Brown-Séquard introduced a physiological dimension by encouraging Jackson to study disease as departures from normal states.

An early interest in ophthalmology also had an important bearing on Jackson's neurological career, as not only did he constantly urge ophthalmoscopic examination in all neurological diseases, but also advocated the integration of ophthalmology with other specialities including psychiatry. "I feel more and more convinced", he wrote in 1865/6, "that there are important reasons why ophthalmologists and those physicians practising in insanity should do work in common. Not because defects of sight are particularly associated with mental symptoms, but because the special study of evolution of movement (and sensation) is, I think, best begun at ophthalmic hospitals. And so far as we can know anything definite of mind, it is I suppose, made up of sensory and motor phenomena, the functions of a series of anatomical possibilities in the cerebrum in correspondence with its wide environment as well as the spinal cord with its narrow environment". Jackson's linking of ophthalmology and psychiatry was liable to be misunderstood, so he clarified his meaning in "On the comparative study of diseases of the nervous system" (1889, II, 395), wherein he suggested that a comparative study would "help us to a more realistic explanation of symptomatologies so different as those in a case of paralysis of an external rectus and those in cases of insanity". As he believed that all diseases were evolutionary flaws, it followed that ocular paralysis and psychiatric illnesses were manifestations of a common cause. Further, when Jackson was making these observations, neurosyphilis was prevalent and its protean manifestations came to the notice of physicians, alienists, ophthalmologists, and neurologists alike.

Hughlings Jackson's continued interest in psychological medicine after he was committed to neurology is shown by the fact that in 1866 he joined the Medico-Psychological Association. His hospital practice also gave him ample opportunities of observing the psychiatric manifestations of organic diseases, as he often saw patients with self-inflicted injuries, *delirium tremens*, and confusional states accompanying rheumatic fever, pneumonia, erysipelas, bronchitis, and typhoid. "I think, then, the study of mental diseases may be well *begun* in general hospitals. We have there the advantage of seeing transient and very slight mental disorders" — he wrote in 1875 (I, 119) — "simple cases which are comparatively easily studied. Especially do we see or hear of many degrees of slight and transient disorders of mind after epileptic paroxysms, in the wards and in the out-patient room".

In their survey of the clinical notes at the National Hospital, Hunter and Hurwitz (1961) have shown that several epileptics were wrongly diagnosed as hysterics, and some were treated by hypnosis, practised mainly by C. E. Beevor (1854–1908), who had been trained in Paris by Professor Charcot (1825–97). Hughlings Jackson and David Ferrier occasionally used hypnosis, and Riese and Gooddy (1955) have published clinical notes on an eleven-year-old girl admitted to the National Hospital in 1881. She was reported to have 'catalepsy', but as there was *flexibilitas cerea*, a diagnosis of catatonic schizophrenia would seem more likely. Between the 13th of April and the 6th of June she was hypnotized on at least six occasions with some improvement. In 1879 Ferrier treated another patient with hysterical paraplegia by suggesting "that he should walk well, with a favourable result".

During the latter part of the nineteenth century probably more patients with psychiatric illness were admitted to the National Hospital than in later years. Hunter and Hurwitz, for example, found that a four-year-old boy diagnosed as 'obstinacy' was obviously a psychiatric patient; and those with neurosyphilis were more likely to be admitted to the National Hospital if at all suitable, in order to avoid the stigma of certification, and removal to an asylum. It was such patients with "slightly morbid mental states" that provided Hughlings Jackson with the opportunity of making "profitable comparisons" between psychiatric illness and healthy states, a theme he urged in a lecture to the Hunterian Society in 1892 when recommending the study of delirium in such 'non-cerebral' diseases as pneumonia, bronchitis, and emphysema. In 1895, he reiterated his plea for beginning a "scientific study of insanities" in general hospitals where the "slightest departures from normal are the most easily analysed".

Not only did Hughlings Jackson put his own advice into practice, but he broadened his experience of psychiatry by joining Sir George Savage (1842–1921) on ward rounds at Bethlem Hospital. On these visits Jackson was particularly intrigued by patients who expressed the most bizarre delusions. He recalled, for example, that one of Savage's patients believed that he was "a jar of Indian pickles"; and an 'insane' woman told him that she had "seen some cats going in an open boat to meet our Saviour in the air". During these ward rounds Savage noticed that his colleague tended to avoid too close a contact with chronic patients as his "mind needed order and precision and disorders of the mind only perplexed him. At times he seemed to have a real physical dread of the insane", Savage (1917) continued, "and failed to have anything like the human sympathy that he had for epileptics. He regarded the insane as useless occupiers of beds in asylums". This explanation of Hughlings Jackson's desire for "order and precision" is particularly perspicacious. But his attitude towards chronic psychiatric patients may have been misunderstood, as Charles Mercier (1912) has stated that Jackson behaved in a detached, a seemingly unsympathetic manner towards all chronic patients whom he was unable to help. The sight of unrelievable suffering made him feel uncomfortable and he tended to avoid passing near the beds of such patients. A contributory factor may have been the contrast between the over-crowded and squalid wards of the asylum, and the relatively pleasant surroundings at Queen Square from where (according to Hunter and Macalpine (1974), "the difficult and dirty, the unmanageable and the incurable" were excluded.

Hughlings Jackson also kept in touch with psychiatry through his regular visits to the West Riding Asylum at Wakefield, which James Crichton-Browne had transformed into an outstanding research centre. Crichton-Browne opened a laboratory, organized research, and, in 1871, launched the *West Riding Lunatic Asylum Medical Reports* to publish the observations of the staff as well as other contributions from eminent neurologists, physiologists, and physicians. He invited members of other institutions to use the laboratory facilities, and foremost among them was David Ferrier, who began by improving cortical stimulation technique through using fa-radic, rather than voltaic current, which elicited sustained rather than evanescent movements, and better preserved brain tissue. Before beginning his research, Ferrier had been impressed by Hughlings Jackson's clinical anticipation of the experimental findings of Fritsch and Hitzig (1870), and at Wakefield he set about testing these observations. Ferrier and Jackson shared an intellectual heritage through their close study of the associationist psychologists, and their common interest in the writings of Thomas Laycock. Ferrier had first studied philosophy and the humanities at Aberdeen, where he had been the favourite student of Alexander Bain, Professor of Logic. He then spent a year at Heidelberg reading psychology before beginning medical studies at Edinburgh. After qualifying Ferrier worked as Laycock's assistant, and shared with Jackson other dissimilar interests such as hypno-therapy and the promotion of neurosurgery.

Other distinguished lecturers at Wakefield, and contributors to the *Reports*, included Clifford Allbutt (1836–1935), William B. Carpenter, and Hughlings Jackson. The last men-tioned had several reasons for visiting Wakefield, not the least of them being to witness experimental confirmation of his clinical observations. His visits were also part of his regular holidays in Yorkshire, and inevitably these excursions kept him in touch with psychological medicine. In this respect Crichton-Browne did his utmost to be both instructive and hospitable. He arranged monthly conversaziones at which guests might, after attending lectures, view the demonstrations and exhibitions presenting current psychiatric knowledge in a readily assimilated form. Pathological specimens of various brain lesions associated with psychiatric syndromes were shown. Microscopic examination of sections of brain tissue could be conducted; and the allegedly normal and abnormal distribution of cerebral convolutions were displayed. A photographic gallery depicted patients' physiognomy, which was thought to correlate with their psychiatric illnesses.

There were maps illustrating the distribution of psychiatric disorders together with others showing the incidence of suicide in England and Wales. Undoubtedly Hughlings Jackson was fascinated by his visits to Wakefield. He became a lifelong friend of Crichton-Browne and the most prolific contributor to his *Asylum Reports*.

In 1888, during the Presidency of Dr. Frederick Needham, Hughlings Jackson delivered to the members of the Medico-Psychological Association an address "On post-epileptic states", subtitled: "A contribution to the comparative study of insanities", in which he recommended both scientific and clinical studies. "Without a considerable clinical knowledge of cases", he wrote (I, 377), "no one is fitted to begin the scientific, comparative, study of nervous diseases. For the scientific study of insanities a very wide clinical knowledge is necessary. It would never do to confine attention to cases described in textbooks by alienist physicians, to what I may call 'orthodox' cases of insanity. Not being an alienist physician I say this, and what follows in the present section, under correction by the Members of this Society, who of necessity know very much more of 'diseases of the mind' than I do. I should not presume to address alienist physicians on their special subject had I not the hope that from a long study of simpler diseases of the nervous system, I might contribute something of at least indirect value for the elucidation of the most complex problems they have to deal with. In a later section I shall urge a study of cases of abnormal mental affections, many of which are not, in a clinical regard, cases of insanity at all, and, so far as I know, are not dwelt upon in books on insanity". Needham opened the discussion by describing Jackson's address as being "of such complexity and elaborateness" as "to take away one's power of expression if not power of thought". Savage then referred to an American report on the use of nitrous oxide as a means of uncovering insanity, and suggested that its comparison with epilepsy might be fruitful. After a discussion of the forensic aspects of epileptic automatisms, Hack Tuke suggested that a study of pre-epileptic impulses should be made.

Hughlings Jackson again modestly disclaimed any special knowledge of mental disorders in his contribution to the discussion of 'Inhibition'. "Not being an Alienist physician", he wrote in 1888 (II, 481n), "my experience of these degrees of post-epileptic states is small. I deal with cases I see, and speak subject to correction by those whose experience of what are called mental diseases, is greater than mine".

Thus through the teachings of Hack Tuke and Thomas Laycock, and by his own study of psychiatric illnesses in general hospitals; through visits to Bethlem and Wakefield, Hughlings Jackson kept in touch with clinical psychiatry. He supplemented these observations by wide reading which included the quarterly issues of the *Journal of Mental Science*, and later through his editorial cooperation with Crichton-Browne and Bucknill.

In tracing Hughlings Jackson's psychiatric background it is not intended to imply that he was a psychiatrist any more than it would be justified to regard him as an ophthalmologist on account of his constant advocacy of the use of the ophthalmoscope in neurological practice. Essentially he was a neurologist with a secondary interest in neuropsychiatry.

A Contribution to Gilles de la Tourette Syndrome

In 1864, when Hughlings Jackson was a 29-year-old assistant physician at the London Hospital where he had been appointed two years earlier, he admitted a 13-year-old boy with 'twitching of his face'. Five or six years previously the patient had been frightened by a man shouting "bloody", and thereafter he continuously repeated this oath for three days and nights. A year later, he developed 'choreiform' movements mainly on the right side, and continued to swear frequently even in church, and, much to his own annoyance, tended to blow out a candle involuntarily when reading by its light. This picture of multiple tics, compulsive utterances, with coprolalia, echolalia, and respiratory dyskinesia in a boy of 8 or 9 is typical of Gilles de la Tourette syndrome, and here is Jackson's[1] first brief account of it at the end of a contribution on "Loss of speech and hemiplegia on the right side; recovery of power to swear" (1864): "I have a patient, the subject of chorea, who, for several years, has been in the habit of saying, quite involuntarily, the word 'bloody'. A few years ago, he was frightened by a man shouting the word after him. The fright produced chorea, and, if I may use such a term, chorea of his mind, too; as, for three days, he said the word 'bloody', and little else; and now he ejaculates it occasionally. The mental process for saying that word, is as little under control as a few of the muscles of his face are, for the twitching of which he is now attending the London Hospital". Jackson gave more clinical details to a reporter from the *Medical Times and Gazette* (1865), and this account[2] appeared a year later:

Involuntary ejaculations following fright — subsequently chorea.
(Under the care of Dr. HUGHLINGS JACKSON)

There seems to be nothing more certain than that fright is often followed by chorea. The history is frequently too definite to leave it doubtful that there is some relation. For instance, a child at the London Hospital had chorea soon after seeing a man in an exhibition eat a live rat; another soon after her mother fell downstairs. In a third, the following case, there were circumstances which rendered it quite certain that fright had much to do with developing certain quasi-mental symptoms in a patient who a year later had chorea. Yet it is scarcely likely that fright can be considered as a sole cause. It could not, one would think, produce chorea nearly limited to one side of the body, as it is now and then. The probability is, that there is some previous enfeebled condition of the nervous system which renders it liable to suffer from undue excitement. At all events, fright produces chorea most frequently in those who have had rheumatism or who have valvular disease. What the condition of the nervous tissue in chorea is we have little evidence. Dr. Russell's examination was nearly negative in its results. Perhaps a minute examination of nervous tissue on Lockhart Clarke's plan might show some change in this motor tract or convolutions near it. So far as we know this has not yet been done. The recent researches of Dr. Beale lead us to hope that many obscure points in cerebral pathology will be at length cleared up. Now that he has succeeded in *working with* a fiftieth (*sic*) of an inch, we may hope to discover what the disease of apparently healthy tissue in such diseases as chorea is.

A boy, 13 years of age, was admitted on August 16 for twitching of the face. Five or six years before he had been frightened by a man shouting the word "bloody" after him. For three days and nights he kept saying this word continually, and for three weeks he said it very frequently. Ever since he has had the habit of ejaculating it occasionally.

A year afterwards he had an attack of chorea, which chiefly affected the right side.

When Dr. Jackson saw him, there was merely a little twitching of the face on each side, and as this had continued for several years treatment was not likely to do much for it. There was no bruit, and he had not had rheumatic fever; he had, however, had scarlet fever some time before the fright. He seemed in good health and looked intelligent, but his mother said that his temper was very bad, and that he would frequently swear. It was then suggested that perhaps he used the word "bloody" in that way, but she replied that he said it when quite calm, and that not unfrequently he ejaculated it in church, to the manifest surprise of those sitting near him. He had another trick, more curious still. He would frequently blow out the candle. He was very fond of reading, and yet sometimes he would suddenly blow out his own candle, much to his annoyance.

In this instance quasi-mental acts were performed without the intervention of the patient's will, even when he was apparently quite conscious. They look like reflex actions, though what the exciting cause is it would be difficult to say. Some patients who cannot talk (who cannot *say* anything)—in cases of loss of speech with hemiplegia on the right side—sometimes swear; but it must be observed that, as a rule, their ejaculations are involuntary, like the boy's just mentioned. In these cases, however, there is nearly always an exciting cause, as anger or surprise. But although the patients swear when vexed, they cannot repeat the oaths when calm. Perhaps some Physicians would class the boy's ejaculations in the same general category with the uncontrollable impulses we sometimes meet with in cases of epilepsy. In the latter, however, there is, Dr. Jackson says, so far as he has observed, more or less unconsciousness. Yet it is possible that this may be but a question of degree. Besides, the important thing is to determine the relation of these morbid quasi-mental actions to healthy mental processes, and not to label them, or the diseases with which they occur, with nosological names. Moreover, to determine their nature, it is a matter of great moment, as a first step, to study exactly the more purely physical symptoms with which they occur, and in each case on its own merits, without particular reference to established groups of disease. Now, it is in some classes of cases of disease of the nervous system hard to say where obviously motor symptoms end and where the purely mental ones begin. Thus there is (in cases of hemiplegia on the right side) every gradation betwixt, on the one hand, a total loss of the power to express ideas, or a loss of knowledge of the relations of words to things, and, on the other, apparently scarcely more than a peculiar motor defect in talking—an ataxy of articulation. And sometimes in the same case we find that the patient makes mistakes in words, and also articulates badly. In the case the subject of these remarks there are (1) involuntary ejaculations, (2) involuntary and yet complete actions, and (3) local spasm or twitching of muscles. We may, perhaps, find all shades, degrees, and analogies betwixt obvious and coarse motor reflex actions, and disorder of what Dr. Laycock has described as the reflex function of the brain. We may thus analyse with some success, from the study of phenomena which are superficial and simple, more hidden and intricate mental conditions.

In 1885, when a member of Charcot's staff, Georges Gilles de la Tourette[3] (1857–1904) described the syndrome that bears his name, he called it 'tics convulsifs'. But Charcot regarded it as a distinct clinical entity and suggested the present eponym.

Earlier, in 1825, another Frenchman, J. M. G. Itard (1774–1838), described the same syndrome in a seven-year-old girl who developed tics and uttered bizarre cries and a meaningless jumble of words. Some years later, after her marriage, the Marquise de Dampierre had an exacerbation of symptoms, and this distressing combination of involuntary ejaculations of obscenities with the lady's otherwise refined manners caused her to withdraw from society. She lived as a recluse for the next 70 years and died over 90 still cursing.

Hughlings Jackson was particularly interested in speech disorder, including swearing, which he neatly defined as "propositions which are intellectually dead" being little more than "detonating commas" or "verbal missiles". But concerning medical priorities he would not have been in the least perturbed to know that his contribution had been overlooked as he was more interested in determining "the relation of these morbid quasi-mental actions to healthy mental processes, and not to label them, or the diseases with which they occur, with nosological names".

References

[1] Jackson, J. Hughlings (1864), "Loss of speech and hemiplegia on the right side; recovery of power to swear", *Clin. Lect. and Reports to the London Hosp.*, 1, pp. 452–3.

[2] Jackson, J. Hughlings (1865), "Involuntary ejaculations following fright—subsequently chorea", *Med. Times & Gaz.*, 1, p. 89.

[3] Gilles de la Tourette, G. (1885) "Étude sur une affection nerveuse caractérisée par de l'inco-ordination motrice accompagnée d'écholalie et de coprolalie (jumping latah myriachit)", *Arch. de neurol.*, 9, pp. 19–42, 158–122.

[4] Itard, J. M. T. (1825) "Mémoire sur quelques fonctions involontaires des appareils de la voix", *Arch. gén. de méd.*, 8, pp. 385–407.

Mind–Brain Relations

Hughlings Jackson first discussed the relations of mind and brain in "On the anatomical and physiological localization of movements in the brain" (1875), where he drew attention to the confusion caused by mixing psychological and physiological terms. He returned to this theme in "On post-epileptic states" (1888), and argued that it is wrong to state that a patient in a post-ictal coma cannot move because he has lost consciousness: among other misconceptions are the supposition that an emotion can accelerate the heart-beat, or that ideas, or sensations, can provoke movements. Jackson believed in the strict separation of mental and nervous matters, and Mercier (1912) recalled that he dismissed as 'scientific blasphemy' all expressions implying an interaction between body and mind such as 'psycho-motor' or 'centre of ideas'. The separation of mental states from their anatomical substrata allowed him to concentrate on the sensori-motor activities of the nervous system, and in "On the localization of movements in the brain" (1875) he wrote (I, 52): "I do not concern myself with mental states at all except indirectly in seeking their anatomical substrata. I do not trouble myself about the mode of connection between mind and matter. It is enough to assume a parallelism. That along with excitations or discharges of nervous arrangements in the cerebrum, mental states occur, I, of course, admit; but how this is, I do not inquire; indeed, so far as clinical medicine is concerned, I do not care".

In his Croonian lectures (1884) Hughlings Jackson gave a more detailed explanation of the doctrine of concomitance, according to which states of consciousness, synonymous with states of mind, are utterly different from nervous states; and for every mental state there is a correlated nervous state. Although mental and physical states occur in parallel, there is no interference of one with the other. Jackson illustrated psychophysical parallelism by tracing successive events accompanying perception. A visual image stimulates an unbroken physical circuit, with complex reflex action, from the periphery passing through the highest centres to reach the muscular periphery. The visual image, a purely mental state, arises during (not from) activity of the two highest links in this purely physical chain.

When accused of adopting psychoneural concomitance to "evade a charge of materialism", Jackson then considered three body–mind theories in "Remarks on evolution and dissolution of the nervous system" (1887). He began disarmingly, by frankly admitting that he was "not competent to discuss the metaphysical question of the *nature* of the relation of mind to nervous activities" (II, 84), which, in any event, he regarded as an insoluble problem. In its simplest form Cartesian dualism holds that mind and body, though separate and distinct, may causally interact. But interactionism implies that a mental event can cause a physical one, a supposition which Hughlings Jackson strongly opposed, and hence he dismissed dualism as "the least worthy of attention" (II, 85). Indeed, Jackson's tenacious adherence to parallelism was such that Mercier (1912) recalled that he stated that if any one could convince him of the validity of an interacting dualism he would "abandon the study of the nervous system" as this would mean "the negation of law".

Next Jackson considered whether activities of the highest centres, and mental states, are one and the same, or different

aspects of the same phenomenon. This psychophysical identity theory was adopted by Jackson's contemporaries
Alexander Bain and Thomas Huxley (1825–95). Its adher-
ents asserted that mind and matter, though capable of being
logically distinguished, are really different expressions of a
single material reality. In Huxley's view consciousness is a
by-product of bodily mechanisms which does not exert any
modifying influence on them, similar to the whistle on a
steam engine that functions without affecting the locomotive's
machinery. Jackson rejected Huxley's sceptical materialism
for several reasons. First, he felt that it over-simplified a complicated problem, by assuming "that there is nothing to
explain" (II, 85); and also ". . . to merely solidify the mind
into a brain, is to make short work of a difficult question".
Second, he could not accept that mental functions should be
discussed materialistically. "A medical man's aim should be
to deal with what are called diseases of the mind (really diseases of the highest cerebral centres)", he wrote (I, 367), "as
materialistically as possible. But to be thoroughly materialistic
as to the nervous system we must not be materialistic at all as
to mind". He considered, too, that a "materialistic explanation
of mental states" could cause neglect of their anatomical
substrata, but in a footnote, added that he would be prepared
to accept a modification of this theory. Mind, he believed, is
the reality behind all cerebral activity which, in turn, co-
ordinates bodily functions. But instead Jackson adopted a
non-controversial alternative theory, and thereby avoided the
polemics, exposure to which had impelled Huxley (1893)
to retaliate against his most vociferous clerical critics: "It
really would be well if ecclesiastical persons would reflect
that ordination, whatever deep-seated graces it may confer,
has never been observed to be followed by any visible increase in the learning and logic of its subjects". Instead
Jackson turned to parallelism, and mistakenly included
Spencer, Bain, and Huxley as supporters. This theory appealed
to Jackson by sharply dividing mind and body into two

irreducible terms, so that "there is no physiology of the mind any more than there is a psychology of the nervous system" (I, 417). By avoiding an epistemological argument parallelism had the dual appeal of allowing Jackson "to study the most complex diseases of the nervous system more easily". Although he was prepared to accept that parallelism might be regarded as an unsatisfactory theory for "those who seek an explanation of mental states" (which was not his purpose), Jackson went so far as to argue that even if the theory proved unacceptable on philosophical grounds, it should, nevertheless, be adopted as "an artifice" in order to facilitate the study of neurology. Thus Jackson firmly refused to be drawn beyond the simple statement that mentation takes place during cerebral function and is concomitant with brain activity.

Before moving on from mind–body theories, mention should be made of Cobb's (1952) more recent assessment of the adherence of American neurologists. Although "some idealists" might favour dualism, and others agree with Jackson, Cobb considered that "the majority . . . now believe that activities of the highest centres and mental states are one and the same thing". And in support of his opinion he quoted Brain's (1951) assertion that some events in the brain are simultaneously physiological and mental. Freud and Sherrington also adopted parallelism, which Angel (1961) regarded as a useful theory for understanding "experiments on the neural basis of mind". But he modified Jackson to read "every kind of mental process is correlated with a specific *kind* of cerebral process" which provides a rationale for psychophysiology.

Hughlings Jackson often suggested that neurological problems should be discussed empirically and scientifically, meaning clinically and physiologically. Jackson always assumed a physiological rôle in which psychology was the subordinate discipline. In other words, Hughlings Jackson swept psychology under the physiological carpet, although he could never resist taking a peep at this autonomous science. "Our concern as medical men is with the body" he wrote (II, 85), "If there be such a thing as disease of the mind, we can do nothing for it. Negative and positive mental symptoms are for us, only signs of what is not going on, or what is going on wrong in the highest sensori-motor centres". Thus Jackson regarded psychiatric symptoms as manifestations of brain disturbances caused by increased activity of the uncontrolled and undamaged layers of the highest cerebral centres in consequence on a dissolution. He then interpreted this complex symptomatology into simpler physiological components. Whenever he discussed mind and brain relations Jackson dismissed his critics in an uncharacteristic and rather cavalier fashion. For example, when he was rebuked for adopting Leibniz's 'two clock theory' he airily retorted (II, 84), "it may be; it matters nothing for medical purposes whether it is or is not".

A distinguished critic, on philosophical rather than medical grounds, was Morton Prince (1891), who argued that if mental activities are assumed to be in parallel, and set apart from nervous activities, then mind cannot enter into events governing human actions. Such a theory is unacceptable, suggested Prince, on account of its rejection of the volitional initiation of actions. Further, he argued that if mind is to be regarded as the reality behind cerebral activities, then there cannot be two separate processes in the same individual occurring synchronously side by side. On the contrary, Morton Prince affirmed that there is only a mental process governing physical actions, but Jackson avoided entering into a philosophical argument, and did not reply.

In the third Hughlings Jackson Lecture, Broadbent (1903) stated that Jackson adopted the principle of concomitance in order to make a clean break with 'faculty' psychology, and also to get neurologists to "bear in mind that in disease they have to deal with structure and function of nervous centres". A similar point has been made by Engelhardt (1972) and (1975), who states that Jackson's adoption of concomitance encouraged him to "isolate neurology and treat it as a physical science independent of psychology". He agreed, too, that Jackson's adoption of concomitance allowed him to replace the "notion of psychological 'faculties' with a physiological concept of integration and co-ordination and to develop a purely physiological notion of cerebral localization".

The Experimental Psychoses

Hughlings Jackson regarded toxic states induced by alcohol, belladonna, and cannabis as model psychoses, uniform dissolutions, or reversals of evolution. Hence his hypothesis on evolution and dissolution occurring within a hierarchical conception of nervous system function should be considered briefly. Essentially Jackson regarded the central nervous system as a series of sensori-motor levels representing impressions and movements superimposed on one another, and developed within the evolutionary scale. He delineated a hierarchy of three hypothetical physiological levels in which there is a re-representation of functions subserved by the lower level. Hughlings Jackson went to some pains to define his meaning of representation. He did not regard it as being similar to the representation of a borough in Parliament but rather that a higher centre *is* the lower one raised to a higher power.

The lowest level, comprising the cord, medulla, and pons, has a relatively fixed and restricted representation of functions including such automatic ones as respiration and circulation. The middle level, whose anatomical substrata are the motor and sensory cortices, and the ganglia of the corpus striatum, re-represents movements of all parts of the body (rather than groups of muscles), in wider scope and with more variability of response. Jackson's highest level is the frontal cortex, where all motor activity is triply represented in most complex movements, but in different arrangements from those at lower levels. Motor and sensory centres of the highest level represent the 'organ of mind', or the anatomical substrata of consciousness.

During evolutionary ascent there is an increase in the factors of differentiation (i.e. greater complexity), specialisation (i.e. greater definiteness), integration (i.e. a wider range of representation), and co-operation (i.e. a greater degree of association). The highest sensori-motor centres are constantly evolving and represent the physical basis of mind.

Jackson integrated his reflex doctrine of the brain with evolutionary function, and postulated that each reflex, as well as performing its own specific function, inhibited the activities of lower ones. The highest levels being the "least organised" in structural terms are functionally the "most perfectly reflex". Another measure of evolution is the ability of nervous centres to function independently.

Dissolution, as the reverse of evolution, is a "taking to pieces", when function is affected in an inverse order. Jackson divided dissolutions into general or uniform, and local ones. A general dissolution, such as that caused by the toxic effects of alcohol, involves the whole brain, whereas local dissolutions may be unilateral or bilateral, and involve either motor or sensory pathways. Many local dissolutions are disorders of awareness manifested neurologically as agnosia, apraxia, aphasia, and body image disturbances. As Jackson regarded the frontal lobes as the centres of mental activities, lesions there cause paralysis, rather than restricted movements of muscle groups, as in the complete immobility found in frontal lobe syndromes. Among other local dissolutions, Jackson included G.P.I. and melancholia, affecting, he thought, the frontal lobes and the posterior cortex respectively, together with post-ictal mania and coma.

In Jackson's opinion, a dissolution is equivalent to being reduced to a lower level of evolution. This involves loss of the least organised, most complex, and most voluntary functions, and implies retention of the more organised, less complex, and more automatic ones. A double process is involved in all dissolutions. There is loss, or suspension of function, giving rise to negative symptoms combined with the emergence of the more obtrusive positive symptoms resulting from the 'letting go' of lower centres after removal of higher control. He emphasized that a positive sign, such as an involuntary movement, cannot be caused by a brain lesion ('nothing cannot be the cause of something') but only through the removal of inhibitory processes.

Hughlings Jackson's study of toxic psychoses as uniform dissolutions was implemented by his wide reading, and in particular, he mentioned H. C. Wood's *A Treatise on Therapeutics* (1874), which included the author's account of the effects of a large dose of cannabis. "A careful study of the abnormal mental condition this distinguished physician records, will, I submit, in a scientific regard", he wrote in 1895 (II, 484), "be more profitable than that of most cases of insanity ordinarily so-called". Clearly he was primarily interested in cannabis intoxication as a model psychosis rather than a toxic state, although his own observations were mostly limited to alcoholic intoxication.

Alcohol causes a uniform dissolution affecting the highest nervous centres, and progresses through middle and lowest levels in compound order. Highest centres offer least resistance while lowest ones resist longest; otherwise, Jackson adds, death from alcoholic intoxication "would be a very common thing". In a later contribution Hughlings Jackson was able to explain dissolutions, in more detail, by subdividing the highest centres into four hypothetical layers: the uppermost, being the site of most vivid consciousness, is most rapidly rendered functionless by a small quantity of alcohol such as "makes a man not worse but 'better for' liquor" (II, 430). This causes increased mental activity *of a sort* with a greater flow of ideas, but any conversational brilliance is always accompanied by a defect of consciousness manifested as impairment of judgement. More alcohol eliminates more layers causing greater impairment of judgement, more loss of self-control, and a diminished awareness of the surroundings possibly accompanied by garrulousness, high-spiritedness, or emotional instability. Still more alcohol affects the middle level and weakens the musculature in an inverse order to its development, affecting first the most voluntary and special-ised muscles, including those of the tongue, eyelids, face, and limbs, which become progressively more unmanageable, and lastly the bilateral muscles of the thoracic cage. At the same time, speech becomes repetitive, uninhibited, and slurred. In this regression to a more infantile state, the subject cannot think without speaking, as exemplified by the loose-tongued drunkard. Loss of voluntary power is accompanied by increased automatic action, and the subject is reduced to "a more automatic condition of mind", involving descent from the more special and intellectual, to the general and more animal 'faculties'. At a later stage the subject may become boisterous, quarrelsome, or amatory, and Jackson agreed with De Quincey that the expression 'disguised by liquor' should be reversed to 'disguised by sobriety'. After an even greater quantity of alcohol the subject goes beyond the excitement stage, and his movements become more feeble; he gets more drowsy, losing co-ordination of the finer, and later of the grosser, movements and eventually passes into a coma. He mentioned that he had on several occasions seen comatose patients at the London Hospital, where they had been admitted after drinking raw spirits.

In Jackson's opinion drunkenness is modified, not only by the depth of dissolution, but also by the personality of the drinker. An irrascible man, as distinct from one of placid temperament, is more likely to become violent when drunk. Another modifying factor is the rapidity of the 'reduction' as when the subject passes directly into a stuporose state.

Jackson compared delusions in alcoholism with a 'mistake'

made by an eminent physician who had inadvertently drunk a large quantity of belladonna. When prescribed potassium bromide, the doctor mistook it for mineral water. Jackson argued that similar 'mistakes' may occur in an alcoholic psychosis when slight external impressions provoke elaborate, though uncorrected, subjective states. He gave, as an example, the case of a drunken man who, when lying in a pig-sty, where he was disturbed by the pigs' snouts, exclaimed "Don't tuck me in!" In "The comparative study of drunkenness" (1874) and "Remarks on dissolutions of the nervous system as exemplified by certain post-epileptic conditions" (1881), Hughlings Jackson offered an explanation of alcoholic illusions in terms of Helmholtz's theory. He thought that illusions may occur from intraocular *muscae volitantes*, which in healthy states are projected as sparks or black dots, but in alcoholic intoxication may be mistaken for rats, mice, snakes or lice.

Hughlings Jackson then warned about the difficulty of distinguishing between alcoholic intoxication, head injury, and cerebral haemorrhage, admitting that in some instances differentiation "may be impossible". He had earlier reported on a fatal case of meningeal haemorrhage in which the patient was violent and abusive, while making purposive movements. In "On neurological fragments" he stated that one or two hours after a head injury the clinical picture may resemble that of drunkenness. "I was once consulted by letter on the case of a clergyman", he wrote (1892, p. 52), "who was accused of drunkenness . . . I was able to say that the condition described might have resulted from an injury to the head the patient had had. It is to be borne in mind that . . . after an injury to the head the patient may act elaborately, if foolishly, whilst "unconscious"; that on his recovery he remembers nothing of his strange doings—a thing evidently of medico-legal importance".

He then discussed belladonna poisoning, mainly on the basis of reports by his London Hospital colleagues,

Drs. Gossett-Brown and Fraser. Atropine acts mainly by depressing circulation, respiration, and digestion rather than on the 'organ of mind'. Atropine, he believed, dilates the pupils by paralysing the ciliary muscles, which causes visual aberrations by affecting the uppermost layer of the highest centres. Jackson believed that atropine poisoning causes micropsia, and remarked on the significance of one patient's statement that objects appeared to be a long way off. Hence he argued that it is superfluous to postulate involvement of a so-called cortical 'visual centre'.

When discussing cannabis intoxication, Hughlings Jackson was particularly interested in the concomitant sensation of an apparent prolongation of time sense as mentioned by Wood. "Among other things there was the 'sense of prolongation of time', a subject of great psychological interest; this occurs in dreams and in some cases of ordinary delirium". Jackson's hypothesis on time sense appears in "Remarks on evolution and dissolution of the nervous system" (1887) (II, 116), and is both ingenious and complicated. Time is measured by subjective standards or constants as well as by obvious objective ones such as clocks. He postulated that the physical basis of the time standard is some "rhythmically acting organ represented in the highest centres, most probably the heart's systole". In the lowest centres, the heart is represented in its more menial role of adjusting the circulation to bodily needs, but, he believed, internal evolution brings about a more independent and detailed representation in the highest centres which represents the nervous elements of the time standard. Jackson defined this constant as the most perfect and simple rhythm, or succession of events, occurring at exactly equal intervals independent of external sequences, and constituting part of the substratum of subject consciousness. In perception the subject has knowledge of 'actual' time as the highest centres are strongly engaged with the lower ones, but when thinking of time he is only aware of 'ideal' time as the rate of succession of his own ideas when only the highest motor and sensory centres are engaged. In cannabis intoxication there is a shallow dissolution of the uppermost nervous arrangements unleashing increased activity of the intact layer immediately below, which now becomes uppermost. But this increased activity of a projected objective mental state is out of proportion to the physical basis of the unchanging time constant in the substratum of subject consciousness. Acceleration of ideation, he believed, creates a subjective, but erroneous, impression of the prolongation of time. Riese (1954) has criticised Jackson's explanation, doubting whether any physical rhythm could be other than a comparative standard. In another contribution Riese (1967) argues that as the brain is the subject of evolutionary progression there cannot then be an unvarying time standard or a 'physical absolute'. Further as all parts of the brain are interdependent one part cannot, therefore, become completely independent of the others. And if the time constant, as Jackson believes, is 'self-acting', then a metaphysical element is introduced and its physical basis cannot be determined. An unchangeable frame of reference such as an absolute time constant, argues Riese, must remain an *ideal* standard which "defies any empirical frame of reference".

Consciousness, Perception, and Ideation

"No one should attempt to write on the subject of consciousness from a medical standpoint", wrote Cobb (1952), "without going back to Hughlings Jackson. He probably said more significant things about consciousness and its clinical variations in epileptic and psychotic patients than any other physician". One of the best interpretations of Hughlings Jackson's views on consciousness has been made by Denis Williams (1958), who drew attention to his "much wider and higher" conception of the conscious state. Jackson believed that consciousness represents the whole person mentally while its anatomical sensori-motor substrata represent the whole person physically. He stressed that, though states of consciousness occur in parallel with nervous states, they are utterly different from them. Consciousness, in Jackson's opinion, is a relative state, concomitant with the 'engagement' of reflex actions of the highest centres, and depends on the integration of sensations, ideas, and percepts up to the highest conceptual achievements. And when consciousness is disturbed, the disturbance must be in the highest nervous centres. "Consciousness is not an unvarying independent entity", he wrote (I, 242). "Consciousness arises during activity of some of those of our highest nervous arrangements by which the correspondence of the organism and its environment is being affected". As it is not a separate entity, 'faculty', or single state, consciousness cannot be localised in any part of the brain. "There is no such entity as consciousness;" he wrote (I, 158-9), "in health we are from moment to moment differently conscious. Consciousness varies in kind and degree according as the parts of the brain in activity are different, and according to the degree of their activity; and it varies in depth." On loss of consciousness Jackson wrote (I, 221): "The physiology of loss of consciousness is clear. It is loss of *use of* the highest of all nervous processes — those evolved out of all lower nervous centres". And he discussed loss of consciousness in terms of other symptoms of brain disease (I, 185-6) "Loss of consciousness is not a symptom utterly different from other symptoms. It is not to be dismissed from analysis as a mysterious epiphenomenon or complication. Consciousness is mysterious, but *loss* of consciousness in cases of disease is to be considered on the same method as other nervous symptoms".

Jackson discussed various levels of consciousness occurring in epileptic states, and in all mental disorders he believed that there is a defect of object consciousness and increased subject consciousness. "In every insanity", he wrote (II, 414), "with one obvious exception (complete dementia), there is a double symptomatic condition, a condition of two opposite mental elements, one negative, and one positive (or superpositive) . . . There is in every insanity (1) negatively, defect of consciousness (loss of some consciousness), and there is (2) the consciousness remaining." His conception of the major psychoses as disorders of both the highest centres, and of consciousness, has been described by Brain (1958) as being "of current value". As is often found in Hughlings Jackson's writings, the most concise summary of his ideas on consciousness is consigned to a footnote in a paper entitled "On temporary paralysis after epileptiform and epileptic seizures. A contribution to the study of dissolution of the nervous system" (1881). Here Jackson mentions will, reason, and emotion in order to simplify his explanation of the holistic nature of consciousness because he had long since rejected 'faculty' psychology. "I dare say it may be denied that in some slight cases of insanity there is only defect of consciousness", he wrote in *Brain* (I, 323n), "partly because it is erroneously inferred that what is clinically called insensibility is meant. Yet probably some of those who would deny defect of consciousness in a slight case of insanity would tacitly admit it by saying that the patient's judgment, power of attention, emotional control or will was defective. A person has not got a consciousness in addition to will, memory and emotion; these are only names applied to artificially distinguished aspects of consciousness; defective judgment etc. is defect of consciousness".

Jackson defined subject consciousness as an awareness of the self in the widest and highest sense, and object consciousness as the awareness of the environment as interpreted by the self. He illustrated these differences in the simple statement "I see a brick", in which subject consciousness is symbolised by 'I' and object consciousness by 'brick'. In his earliest papers, including those "On the scientific and empirical investigation of epilepsies" (1874/6), and "Psychology and the nervous system" (1879) Jackson gave a strict anatomical localization of subject and object consciousness but later he became more flexible. Object consciousness is located, he believed, in the right posterior and left anterior cerebral lobes, and subject consciousness in the right anterior and left posterior cerebral lobes. The substrata of subject consciousness precede object consciousness, and are a relatively unchanging standard, whereas object consciousness is constantly changing. The uppermost layer of the highest centres, being the zenith of evolution, is the least organized, least automatic, most complex, most voluntary and represents the substrata of object consciousness. Subject consciousness, being more organized and automatic, is represented immediately below. Subject consciousness represents the whole body

in reverse order. Jackson supported these assumptions with a
clinical example. He argued that the brilliance displayed by a
mentally over-fatigued person is the result of increased
"excitement of subject consciousness *permitted* by slight and
partial exhaustion of the substrata of object consciousness"
(I, 246).

In "Remarks on evolution and dissolution of the nervous
system" (1887) Jackson became more flexible, defining subject consciousness as "an awareness of our existence as individuals . . . having the objective states making up for each, the
(his) Universe . . ." (II, 96). Riese (1954) has pointed out
that in correcting his earlier too rigid and regional localisation
of the anatomical substrata of subject and object consciousness,
Jackson substituted consciousness of self, self-consciousness,
or better still, just 'self', ending in a footnote: "Strictly, of
course, 'I' covers both subject and object consciousness. It
stands for a person" (II, 93n). Instead of ideas coming into
consciousness, Jackson believed that they "come out of subject consciousness and then constitute object consciousness".
Later he recognised the impossibility of detaching objective
states of consciousness from subjective ones, and conceded
that it is subjective states "out of which come all states of
consciousness"; and his notion of the body image is also
based on subject consciousness. "I submit that the units
making up that division of the highest centres which I call the
anatomical substrata of subject consciousness represents [*sic*]
(properly re-represents) all parts of the body mainly sensorily,
in relation to one another. Each unit is the whole division in
miniature, but each is, if the expression may pass, the whole
of it in *different* miniature" (II, 96). Progression from simple
states of consciousness to the unity of the person or self-
consciousness is one of Jackson's fundamental tenets, as is
apparent from his discussion of the consciousness of a pin-
prick, when ". . . physically, the nervous impulses starting
from a point on the periphery pricked 'travel' to units of the
highest centres *universally* representing, and not to units

representing one part of the back only" (II, 97). Before leaving the subject of consciousness Jackson's meaning of 'double consciousness' should be considered. He used it in two different senses. As well as subject and object consciousness, Jackson believed that there are two distinct states of object consciousness.

A Jacksonian influence has re-emerged in Purdon Martin's "Consciousness and its disturbances" (1949) although he incorrectly assumed that Jackson regarded consciousness as a epiphenomenon. Consciousness is associated with cortical activity, and is maintained by sensory excitation, causing awareness of the bodily self in relation to the environment or object consciousness. He tentatively suggests that subject consciousness or consciousness of the self may be a mind–body image analogous with the body image. Purdon Martin introduces the term 'sectional' disturbance of consciousness involving loss of awareness of a part of the self or of its environment. Such selective cortical lesions involve disturbances of the body image, anosognosia, 'dreamy' states, and the psychical seizures of temporal lobe epilepsy.

The fact that Hughlings Jackson considered consciousness to be synonymous with mind or mentation has been criticised by Cobb (1952), who regards it as an attitude of mind, and one of its components. And Schiller's (1952) mention of the survival of "some of Jackson's pioneering concepts of consciousness" is probably a reference to the writings of Henri Ey and Jan Mazurkiewicz, whose modifications of Jacksonian theory they reapplied in psychiatry. Hughlings Jackson's views on consciousness have been neatly summarised by Riese (1954) as a tendency "to conceive man's world and experiences as shaped by man's consciousness".

But Jackson's belief that percepts are externalised through projection has been demonstrated to be invalid by Brain (1951), and he himself was aware of its shortcomings. When reconsidering the problem in "Words and other symbols in mentation" (1893) he wrote (II, 211): "Of course, I do not

mean by using the term 'projected' that the image, part of
our consciousness, is, or is also, something outside us; the
term is only a device for expressing the 'seeming' spoken of;
extrusion of the image is not meant". He does, however,
argue that a percept is an objective psychical construction
like an idea, illusion, or hallucination.

The two components of consciousness, awareness and
reactivity, are the object of an erudite discussion by Denis
Williams (1958). A subject is aware that he is conscious, and
others assume so, too, on account of his appropriate reactions.
Thus, as with other neuronal functions, there are motor and
sensory components of consciousness. There are variations,
too, in the form of consciousness, as in sleeping or waking,
and also in the level of consciousness. Williams defines sleep
as a state of 'lowered reactivity and selective awareness'.
Usually a disturbance of consciousness affects awareness and
reactivity equally, but occasionally reactivity may be diminished while awareness is unaltered as in a stuporose state or
akinesia with mutism.

Perception and ideation, which are affected in delirious
states, are also part of consciousness, and Jackson explained
them along similar lines. He related perception and ideation
to cerebral reflex action, and in the expression 'I see a brick'
states that a vivid image of a brick is aroused when reflex
action is "complete and strong" involving the highest motor
and sensory centres with their lowest equivalents. The concomitant image is, therefore, vividly and definitely projected.
But when thinking of a brick only a faint image is evoked,
and reflex action is confined to the highest motor centres and
the concomitant image is faint and indefinitely projected.
Jackson regarded images as being triply compounded in terms
of their faintness or vividness, their association with already
organised or organising images, and their feeble or strong
reference to the environment. But it should be mentioned
that in his later writings he did not draw such an abrupt
distinction between subjective and objective states. A state is

more subjective, he thought, when more leading images are associated with already organised ones, and it is more objective when associated with images being organised.

The physical basis of the 'organ of mind' is made up of innumerable audito-visual-articulatory nervous arrangements and their vast numbers of interconnecting fibres. Middle and lower levels, as well as being reservoirs of energy, also act as points of resistance to protect the highest centres from unwanted environmental intrusions. The highest layer of the highest centres forms the anatomical substrata of faint images in object consciousness. But when strongly activated by the sensory periphery the whole sensori-motor chain is engaged and correlates with the substrata of vivid images in object consciousness. As we have seen, the substratum of a 'faint' image is less organised than a vivid one, and hence it is at the topmost part of the corresponding vivid image. In normal mentation these highest nervous centres are continuously forming new combinations in order to 'effect the possible'.

The highest centres, being the most differentiated, have the most numerous lateral lines of integration so that slight discharges during ideation are able only to overcome the resistance of other parts of the highest centres where they are confined. In perception stronger discharges overcome this resistance, and reach the lowest centres as the current flows more downwards and less laterally. Ideation and perception are, in different degrees, objective states being preceeded by subjective ones. But an object cannot be seen, or thought of, unless it has first aroused an image resembling it. And when ideation is more intense then more images appear as part of an 'ideal' environment, while the greater the perception the less are the images organised and the more are they related to the actual environment. Greater ideation means less perception and with greater perception there is less ideation, so that normal mentation is a rhythm of subjective and objective states. In confirmation of Hughlings Jackson's views on perception and ideation, Golla (1921) recorded the movements

of his larynx when thinking of the successive notes of an
octave. Apart from the difference in amplitudes, he obtained
an identical curve when he sang the octave. Similar reasoning
applies to other sensory modalities such as hearing, smelling,
and tasting.

Delirium and Coma

Before discussing perceptual disturbances during delirium Jackson's meaning should first be determined. In a penetrating conceptual analysis, Berrios (1981) has shown that during the nineteenth century delirium underwent an aetiological and phenomenological redefinition. Delirium is, of course, related to confusion, also used by Jackson in the descriptive sense of 'confusion of thought' occuring in post-ictal states, and not as a diagnostic entity. Jackson never fully defined delirium in a clinical sense as he was more interested in discussing it as a dissolution. But a survey of his writings show that he used delirium in two different senses, and gave clinical examples of non-delirious patients. In "A study of convulsions" (1870), (I, 26n) he first described delirium as "the *disorderly* revival of sensori-motor processes received in the past"; whereas in "On the scientific and empirical investigation of epilepsies" (1874/6) he regarded delirium and hallucinations as "caricatures of healthy mentation" (I, 180). Jackson was slightly more informative in "On affections of speech from disease of the brain" (1878/9), where he defined "simple cases of delirium" as "partial imperception with inferior perception" (II, 168). Imperception was Jackson's term for what later became known as agnosia. Finally in a lecture "On neurological fragments" (1892), pp. 47–50, he widened his description to that of a "transient insanity" in 'non-cerebral' diseases involving a defect of consciousness, and diminished awareness of the surroundings accompanied by hallucinations, illusions, and delusions. He maintained that in delirium the defect of consciousness leads to "a gradually increasing quasi-relation to organized experiences" of former surroundings, and the substitution of "unrealities for realities".

Jackson agreed with Gowers (1888) that delirium should be regarded as an 'insanity'. But in "On temporary mental disorders after epileptic paroxysms" (1875) he used 'delirium' in the French sense of *délire*, and in translation from Falret wrote "delirium chiefly occurs as a consequence of epileptic attacks, recurring at short intervals after a prolonged suspension of the disease" (I, 121n). This passage is from Falret's *Des maladies mentales et des asiles d'aliénés* (1864). Berrios (1981) has shown that by about 1860 *délire* was used to describe aberrant ideas accompanying delirium, but Jackson confused this meaning of delirium accompanying a febrile illness with the delusional state seen in some epileptics. Berrios (1981) has also shown, on the basis of clouding of consciousness, that delirium became separated from the 'insanities' by the end of the nineteenth century, although Jackson consistently referred to the defect of consciousness accompanying "delirium and all other insanities".

A dissolution, such as delirium, causes a loss of independence of the highest centres, with exhaustion of their uppermost layer. This leads to a defect of object consciousness with increased subject consciousness, and thereby reduces mentation to a lower, more organised, and more automatic level. More organised images take the place of less organised ones in activating the substratum of a 'faint' image such as a mentation highest centres act independently of the lowest ones in activating the substratum of a 'faint' image such as a cloud of smoke. When this independence is lost, as in delirium, there is a reduction to a lower evolutionary level. In thinking of a cloud of smoke a vivid image, or a visual hallucination, is now evoked. Likewise words that in a healthy state would be thoughts are now heard. "When a patient is delirious, say during non-cerebral disease, and goes through, in pantomime, the manipulations of his trade", wrote Jackson in "Evolution and dissolution of the nervous system" (1884), (II, 69), "although these operations are exceedingly elaborate in themselves, they are not elaborate to him. They have become deeply automatic, and go on very much by themselves in health; in consequence, in spite of their elaborateness, the persistence of only such actions implies a deeper dissolution than the persistence in another patient of actions equally elaborate, which had not in him become automatic".

The contents of hallucinations are related to topics entering consciousness or unconscious mentation. When the highest centres are unable to function independently of the lower centres the person cannot think in "a complex manner", and his thoughts take on a perceptual form. When 'reduced' to a more automatic condition lower centres function more freely as they are released from control of the highest centres but, as in delirious states, attention is correspondingly weakened. There are such negative symptoms as impaired judgment, a failure to adapt to the surroundings, emotional blunting, and defective perception. An increase in vivid images is revealed in such positive symptoms as hallucinations, delusions, illusions, extravagant conduct, and abnormal emotional states. Thus in delirium the most complex mental functions are the first to be disturbed, and are also the last to recover. Levin (1966) has pointed out that, during recovery, disorientation clears up first while the more complex functions may be disturbed for several days or weeks afterwards. Reduction to a lower and earlier stage of perception causes the patient to mistake the unfamiliar for the familiar, as when he mistakes a nurse for his wife. In Jackson's view, the first stage of recognition normally takes place in the unconscious, or subconscious, with the automatic reproduction of a well-organised symbol-image of a woman, usually that of his wife or mother. By a well-organised symbol-image, Jackson meant the image of a woman well known to him, usually his wife, which is well-organised through having been frequently evoked. Unless there is such a well-organised symbol-image the patient would be unable to recognise the nurse as a woman. It is easier for the patient to recognise a woman as his wife than to realise that she is not his wife. The first is facilitated by long practice, whereas the second requires descrimination and a high level of attention. In health discrimination is made effortlessly but a delirious patient mistakes the unfamiliar for the familiar as the symbol-image of a woman is vividly reproduced in the over-active layer immediately below the exhausted uppermost ones. As we have seen, loss of object consciousness is accompanied by increased subject consciousness, and in delirium arbitrary images, symbol-images, and other vivid images cease to be mere symbols but become 'a general notion', or an 'abstract idea' of a woman. Normally perception, volition, and recollection, being unconscious, take place without any preliminary stage. But when the highest nervous arrangements are *hors de combat*, as in delirium, only the fittest and best-organised images survive, and provide the patient with the best type of mentation possible for him. Recognition is reduced to a lower evolutionary stage when the highest associative processes fail to prevent the combination of specific associations of a given object or situation and hinder their correct identification. The patient is not only lost to his real surroundings, but his actions and conversation are read-justed to some former ideal environment. Hence his illusions are his perceptions, his delusions his beliefs, as his mentation has been reduced to a lower homologue of the healthy state. Levin (1953) has drawn attention to an interesting misidentification in delirious patients. After replying to his physician's questions with such phrases as: "Yes doctor", the patient is then unable to name his vocation. And Jackson criticised the popular statement that a sane man "lives in the real world", whereas an insane man "lives in a world of his own" as being scientifically misleading because everyone, he believed, lives in a world of his own.

Of Jackson's explanation of mistaking the unfamiliar for the familiar, Levin (1945) states that "clinical experience overwhelmingly bears out Jackson's observation . . . Generations of psychiatrists have known that delirious patients are disorientated but have failed to notice that the disorientation is not a hazard but governed by the law that the unfamiliar is mistaken for the familiar". Hughlings Jackson gave several examples of 'mistakes' in delirious states. One patient complained that the man in the next bed had cut a piece out of his blanket as big as a top hat, and when asked how he knew, replied: "Because I saw him". A delirious cabman, standing by his bed, asked Jackson to get in, and when asked: "Where is your cab?" replied with a sneer, that plainly meant "what a fool you must be": "Why here", pointing to the bed. Another patient told him that his friends had brought him two birds in a cage. When Jackson asked to see the cage the patient produced a wire bottle container fixed to the bedside locker and explained that the top was lost. Another patient said: "I've brought this bale from the gateway and want two shillings for it". The 'bale' was, in fact, a folded blanket. In "Words and other symbols in mentation" (1893), (II, 212), Jackson described a girl with an intracranial tumour, who was blind, deaf, and psychotic. She experienced the persistent hallucination of a man, in the corner of the room, mocking her. Jackson stated that the girl regarded her hallucinations as her perceptions, her delusions as her beliefs, and although this explanation confused reality with unreality he queried: "What reality and whose reality? The mocking man was the poor girl's reality; she took a poker to strike him". A genuinely delirious patient was a sack-dealer with erysipelas. When a house surgeon opened a small abscess over his eyelid he became violent and had to be restrained in a straitjacket. Subsequently he embroidered the incident by stating that he had gone to a public house where the landlord had fastened him down with two sacks and poked out one eye. This is an example of the disorderly mentation of delirium with the substitution of unrealities for realities as the patient's delusions had become his beliefs. But not all the patients were delirious: one had a brain tumour, and the cabman was in a state of post-ictal automatism. But Hughlings Jackson never allowed diagnostic niceties to hinder the elucidation of a general neurological principle.

The cabman saw a cab when other observers saw a bed but "to wonder why he did not see it as a bed is like . . . wondering why Esquimaux do not see glass as glass". Jackson elaborated on his phenomenological approach, and argued that each individual has his own perceptual world making up its own intrinsic reality. "It is of no avail for trustworthy witnesses to assert that the patient *could not have seen a cab*, because there was no cab present, and, therefore, that the patient only fancied that he saw one," Jackson wrote in "On post-epileptic states (1888) (I, 384). "Something not himself 'got out of' himself, the image cab, 'out of' the bystanders the image of bed . . . It might be said that the doctrine confuses reality with unreality. But what reality, whose reality? The image cab was the patient's reality; the image bed was the healthy bystanders' reality", and in a footnote added: "I do not say 'image of a cab' and 'image of a bed'. I am not endorsing a crude popular psychological hypothesis that 'real' outer objects, in themselves coloured, shaped, etc. photograph their colour, shape etc. on us. What I call image is a state of mind (each person's), a 'ghost', standing as a symbol of something not us, of the nature of which something we know nothing".

Coma differs from delirium only in the greater extent of paralysis of the nervous centres. In coma there is loss of consciousness together with weakness of vital and other organs. For clinical purposes Jackson divided post-ictal dissolutions into mental confusion, insensibility, and coma. He believed that coma served as paradigm of other mental symptoms. In

post-ictal coma, paralysis not only affects complex movements represented in the highest centres, but extends to the
middle and lowest levels, although some activities do continue.
As an example of purposive actions after cerebral haemorrhage
Jackson mentioned a patient who made elaborate twirling
movements of his moustache. He believed that post-ictal
coma, with paralysis of the universal representation of all
parts of the body in the highest centres, is similar to that
"mental paralysis of insanity". "The conclusion about post-
epileptic coma is very important", he wrote in "On the comparative study of diseases of the nervous system" (1889), (II,
405), "for from it we make the hypothesis that there is paralysis in all cases of insanity, a widespread or universal paralysis
— that is, of a kind corresponding to the universality of representation of the body by the highest centres, which are certainly diseased in cases of insanity".

Hysteria and Dreams

Hughlings Jackson's only interest in hysteria was to exclude it from the diagnosis of epilepsy, which was his paramount concern. As he did not give any aetiological or diagnostic details, nor did he discuss hysteria separately, Temkin (1971) was unable fully to assess his views. But scattered throughout his writings, often half concealed in footnotes, Hughlings Jackson's ideas on hysteria gradually emerge, beginning with his earliest reference in a footnote to "A study of convulsions" (1870). "When a patient does not utter a word, and yet writes well, *and swallows well*", he wrote (I, 20n), "— this fact showing that there is no considerable palsy of the articulatory muscles — we may be almost certain (quite certain, I believe), that he — it is usually *she* — is pretending, or that the defect is 'hysterical', whatever that word may mean". Clearly Jackson preferred the diagnosis of malingering to that of hysteria, and the next brief reference indicates that he accepted the current assumption that sexual continence is an aetiological factor. In "On affections of speech from disease of the brain" (1878/9) (II, 170), he wrote "Let us state the facts. The patients are nearly always boys or unmarried women. The bearing of this is obvious". As supporting evidence Jackson discussed some sudden and dramatic cures of hysteria such as those wrought by faradization of the vocal cords, a violent thunderstorm, the application of various

appliances, mesmerism, wearing a charm, prayer, and the
application of liniment to the back, which underlines his
belief that hysteria is really a form of malingering. This is
confirmed in his illustration of a speechless woman who,
when asked to say 'ah' while her tongue was depressed
with a spatula, pushed the doctor away and exclaimed:
"How can I, with that thing in my mouth?" and (II, 170)
she then added, "Oh, I have spoken!"

As there is no brain pathology in hysteria Jackson suggested
that 'excitement' might precipitate an 'emotional' form of
hysterical aphonia. "I submit that the facts that the patients
do not talk", he wrote (II, 170), "and *do* write and *do* swallow
are enough to show that there is no disease at all, in any sense
except that the patients are hysterical (which is saying nothing
explanatory), or that they are pretending. There can be no
local disease, at any rate". In "On epilepsies and on the after-
effects of epileptic discharges" (1876) Hughlings Jackson
again referred to "the abnormal emotions of hysteria" but
warned against inferring that emotions may cause somatic
disturbances, as such changes are brought on by the effects of
emotion on the viscera and glands. Further Jackson rejected
any distinction between hysteria and malingering on the basis
of unconscious motivation, as is apparent in this extract from
"Remarks on evolution and dissolution" (1887) (II, 85):
"Unconscious states of mind are sometimes spoken of, which
seems to me to involve a contradiction".

Hughlings Jackson then discussed the semantic muddle
arising over the various meanings of 'functional' In "On
the scientific and empirical investigation of epilepsies"
(1874/6) (I, 209) he mentioned that "the neuroses are often
spoken of as functional diseases. This is, I think, an incon-
venient way of using the word" as their morbid anatomy
could only be inferred. 'Functional' was also used to describe
post-ictal over-activity and loss of function after *grand mal*.
On this basis slight hemiplegia, he argued, might also be
termed 'functional', as only a minute amount of nervous tissue

is destroyed. To avoid any confusion Hughlings Jackson never referred to the neuroses (consisting, he believed, of chorea, genuine epilepsy, insanity, neuralgia, and hysteria) as functional illnesses. As their morbid anatomy is unknown, some therefore assumed that there was nothing to be found, whereas others regarded them as neurological diseases, and inferred, without proof, that they were caused by pathological changes in nervous tissue. Hughlings Jackson dismissed this last line of reasoning as 'metaphysical' pathology, and as an example of a 'metaphysical' diagnosis, he drew attention to the assumption that hysterical palsy is caused by paralysis of the will. How could will, an immaterial concept, he argued, produce organic change?

In general Jackson was opposed to a strict nosological classification of diseases, and preferred to study them as dissolutions. Hence he agreed with Sieveking (1858) that certain diseases of the nervous system tended to merge into one another; and quoted from Handfield Jones (1870) that *grand mal* shades off "on one side by *petit mal* into mere vertigo, on another, into hysteria, and chronic choreic convulsions, on a third into delirium, catalepsy, and somnambulism, and a fourth into neuralgia". (I, 203). Jackson was particularly concerned that atypical cases of epilepsy should not be mistaken for hysteria, and in "Remarks on dissolution of the nervous system as exemplified by certain post-epileptic conditions" (1881) (II, 10), wrote: ". . . We shall overlook the epileptic nature of some of our patients' cases altogether; for example, we may mistake epilepsy for hysteria". It is futile, he argued, to discuss the "anatomy, physiology and pathology of the neuroses" before first excluding neurological disease as "there is a morbid change, no doubt a minute one, but we have discovered it". On the other hand, others confidently claimed that the neuroses may occur in "'neurotic' families, interchangeably by inheritance" (II, 388). But Jackson suggested that epilepsy, migraine, and chorea might be caused by plugging of minute cerebral arteries, and here he was in danger of making a 'metaphysical' diagnosis himself. It should be noted, however, that he omitted hysteria, probably because he did not regard it as a true disease. His main concern was to exclude hysteria from the diagnosis of epilepsy, and in "Lectures on the diagnosis of epilepsy" (1879), Jackson subdivided post-ictal automatisms into five groups according to the degree of behaviour disorder manifested. His fifth category was specially delineated in order to distinguish epilepsy from hysteria, as in both conditions a woman "rolls about, struggling and kicking, shouting, laughing, and often tries to bite" (I, 299). Here Jackson depicted the typical, emotional female hysteric; and when discussing 'dreamy' states with slight and transient seizures mentioned that they may be mistaken for "hysteria, indigestion, malaria etc.". He clearly did not regard hysterical automatisms as equivalent to an epileptic 'dreamy' state, although Temkin (1971) has pointed out that here he contradicted a statement attributed to him by Gowers (1881). "The fact" he wrote, "that these [i.e. hysteroid] seizures may succeed attacks of epileptic *petit mal* has been regarded by Hughlings Jackson as evidence that the hysteroid convulsion (like the automatic action p. 118) is always due to the release of lower centres from the control of the higher by the temporary discharge of the latter". Like Temkin, I have been unable to trace such a statement in Jackson's writings; it may, of course, have been wrongly attributed to him. Gowers thought that hysteria was caused by a discharge creating insubordination of the lower centres acting on the morbid states of the brain "such as leads to the manifestations of hysteria, apart from epilepsy". But the accumulation of evidence from Jackson's writings does not support such a theory. On the other hand, Hughlings Jackson referred to hysteria in descriptive, rather than explanatory terms, to denote an emotionally disturbed state occuring mainly in unmarried females, and closely related to malingering. Nevertheless Jackson's recommendation that attempts to elicit the cause should be undertaken by neurologists, rather than 'alienist' physicians, does suggest that he thought that an organic cause of hysteria might be detected.

Sleep, in Jackson's opinion, is a normal dissolution in which subjective and objective rhythms continue at a lower level. During sleep internal evolution is uninterrupted by environmental interferences as the highest centres are protected by the resisting position of the lowest and middle sensory centres. Many recently acquired combinations and organisations are evanescent, and one function of sleep is to sweep away such trivial and unwanted acquirements. In "On post-epileptic states" (1888) Jackson explained that new organisations are made during sleep, when the highest centres are least active and lower ones are in relatively greater activity. These elements of the nervous arrangements are "left to fight it out", and new combinations arise from surviving elements (I, 376).

In "On temporary mental disorders after epileptic paroxysms" (1875), Jackson mentioned that unconscious cerebration (or "the reflex action of Laycock") is active during sleep, involving two halves of thought: those concerned with tracing resemblances and others for noting differences. During sleep the more automatic function of tracing resemblances is active. Symptoms of delirium or insanity are a succession of ideas of organised resemblances.

Hughlings Jackson then compared perception, dreaming, and ideation evoking vivid and faint images whose substrata are the nervous pathways activated when thinking, seeing, or dreaming of an object. In dreams nervous discharges are slightly greater than in ideation. Thus, in Jackson's opinion, the perceptual world of images seen as illusions, hallucinations, dreams, and in healthy states all have equal validity as experiences. He compared the different degrees of dissolution in sleep to similar changes in epilepsy. And to clarify his meaning he subdivided the highest centres into four hypothetical layers. Dissolution of the topmost layer causes a defect of consciousness with increased ideation signifying increased activity of the second layer. This is analogous to sleep with dreaming, and to the 'dreamy' state in epilepsy. Dissolution of the first and second layers brings about loss of consciousness together with elaborate movements and is comparable to sleep with somnambulism. In an equivalent post-ictal state ideation is forgotten but there are various elaborate and complex actions, which he illustrated in the case of a fisherman who underwent a post-ictal automatism during dinner. In pantomime gestures, he pulled out a line from a reel, untied a knot, and took a hook from his pocket to which he fixed an imaginary bait. Finally, when a dissolution involves the three uppermost layers of the highest centres the resulting coma is analogous to 'so called' dreamless sleep and to post-ictal coma.

In "On post-epileptic states" (1888) Jackson argued that dreaming really involves two persons. In a dream a man 'A' temporarily becomes non-existent, when a dreamer 'B' takes over, but on waking 'B' passes away, and 'A' re-emerges. 'B', the dreamer, is 'A' minus the uppermost layer of the highest nervous arrangements *plus* increased activity of the next lower intact evolutionary layer. When 'B' exists there is no such person as 'A'; and 'B's' dream is 'quasi parasitical' in 'A', for as long as he remembers it. Jackson regarded dreaming as a form of morbid mentation as the uppermost layers of the nervous arrangements, being out of action, caused a defect of object consciousness while allowing increased subject consciousness so that the rhythm of mentation goes on at a lower level.

In "Relations of different divisions of the nervous system etc." (1898), Jackson compared dreaming with the 'insanities', as in both there is loss of function of the uppermost nervous arrangements allowing uncontrolled activity of lower ones. The insane man "is in a dream from which awakening is sometimes not possible" (I, 199). The current generated in dreaming is not strong enough to overcome the resistance of the middle level, and is widely irradiated in the highest level. If this irradiation is too weak the dream ceases. In somnambulism the current overcomes middle and lowest levels; but there is not such a wide irradiation, and the dream is forgotten, whereas deepest sleep is dreamless.

Jackson explained the inability of the dreamer to take urgent action, such as covering up or turning away, when naked, as having two causes. First, movements concerned with locomotion are only slightly represented in the highest centres, and secondly the discharge during dreaming corresponds to ideation, and is not strong enough to overcome the resistance of the middle-level motor centres.

Hughlings Jackson was interested in aspects of dreaming before Freud, and Ernest Jones (1953) has commented on similarities in their views. Jackson's exhortation to "find out about dreams, and you will find out about insanity" was re-echoed in Freud's cryptic statement that "dreams contain the psychology of the neuroses in a nutshell". Hughlings Jackson was as succinct as he was informative on the sexual contents of dreams, on which whole books have been written: in "Remarks on the double condition of loss of consciousness and mental automatism following certain epileptic seizures" (1873), he wrote: "People are said to be more immoral in their dreams; strictly their immorality is not kept under; they are reduced to automaticity; only their lower processes are active".

Obsessions and Jokes

On the 1st March 1894 Hack Tuke addressed the Neurological Society on obsessional-compulsive states, or, as he termed them, 'imperative ideas' (II, 482–4). He began by endorsing an earlier recommendation of his former student Hughlings Jackson on the usefulness of studying slight departures from normal mental states. Tuke went on to mention that, although most obsessional states are not incapacitating, as they are only slight deviations from normal, some patients do become so distressed as to seek relief in an asylum. He then admitted that obsessional states had, hitherto, been disregarded in "our official classification of mental disorders". Too often obsessional patients with a secondary depression had been misdiagnosed as melancholics while those with obsessions of a satanic or divine nature were thought to be suffering from delusional insanity. A third group, with vague feelings of nervous exhaustion, tended to be diagnosed as neurasthenics.

In obsessional states certain ideas or words arise with regular and painful frequency, often associated with compulsive actions, when the subject feels impelled to perform certain actions against his will. After giving examples of innocuous obsessional compulsive states, Tuke mentioned that others reached delusional intensity. In attempting to explain them Tuke recalled Thomas Laycock's doctrine of reflex action of the cerebral cortex together with his evolutionary ideas on the nervous system subsequently developed by Hughlings Jackson. He referred also to Jackson's address at the Leeds meeting of the British Medical Association, published as "On the comparative study of the diseases of the nervous system" (1889). Here Jackson suggested that delusions arise from "evolution going on in the remains of a mutilated nervous system, as certainly as his [the patient's] beliefs when sane signified evolution going on in an entire nervous system" (II, 406). Thus Tuke combined the opinions of a former colleague with those of a former student, and concluded that 'imperative ideas' should be regarded as a dissolution of the highest cerebral centres when automatic functions are released from control of more voluntary ones.

During the discussion Hughlings Jackson also referred to his Leeds address, where he stated "that some very grotesque delusions may be a fixation of absurd beliefs in dreams, in cases where a sudden morbid change, or sudden increase of it, has occurred in the brain during sleep . . ." (II, 394). He reached this conclusion from a series of clinical observations, of which he gave four examples. A man always 'felt' his phantom hand in a gripping position similar to that when it was blown off while holding a cylinder. An aphasic railway signalman, whose recurrent utterances were, "Come on", "Come on to me", had had a stroke in front of his signal box, and these phrases were probably his last premorbid utterances. A soldier had an initial epileptic fit when 'numbering off', and afterwards counted after every fit. A woman sustained a fractured skull while laying oilcloth on a staircase. When unconscious, a few hours before her death, she constantly manipulated the counterpane as though laying down oilcloth, but ceased for a time when a nurse told her that "it was properly laid". From these observations Hughlings Jackson concluded that a cerebral lesion may cause a fixation of what is normally a transient mental state. Appropriately modified this hypothesis, he believed, might explain obsessional states, and he tentatively suggested that 'imperative' ideas might arise when the highest centres are gradually removed and positive symptoms develop so slowly that they may pass unnoticed. Thus it may be inferred that a slow dissolution occurring during sleep may cause a fixation of 'imperative' ideas.

At the opening meeting of the Medical Society of London in 1887, Hughlings Jackson addressed the members on the psychopathology of joking (II, 359-64). He considered humour in evolutionary terms beginning with puns, witticisms, and humorous statements each evolved from the other. Jokes, like dreams, he thought, were "slightly morbid mental statements", and he regarded them as "playing at unreality". Jackson suggested that profitable comparisons could be made between them and various physical states. He described all thoughts as 'stereoscopic', or 'diplopic', and examples of 'double consciousness', being concerned, he thought, with resemblances and differences. He compared visual diplopia, with its true and false images, to the "morbid mental diplopia" of insanity.

Punning he regarded as the lowest form of humour, as its riddle combines complete agreement with a vast difference in meaning. As an example, he posed the question: "When is a little girl not a little girl?" Answer: "When she is a little horse [hoarse]". The feeble amusement of such a pun stems from its incongruity, as in the example 'hoarse' provokes the idea of a cold, but 'horse' that of a large quadruped. Jackson regarded punning, therefore, as playing at being foolish. Likewise, he defined a miser as an amateur pauper, and a habitual drunkard as an amateur lunatic.

After describing dreaming as 'physiological insanity', Jackson gave an example of a physician (probably himself) who, having read of the strained relations between European states, dreamed that he had been consulted by Bismarck, for whom he prescribed a course of potassium iodide. This example of the fusion of two dissimilar mental states involving prescribing for a patient, and the unrest of European states, anticipated Freud's theory of the compound nature of dream symbols.

Jackson discussed the parallel development of a sense of humour, and the "power of realistic scientific conception . . . Persons who are deficient in appreciation of jocosities in their degree of evolution", he wrote (II, 360), "are, in corresponding degrees, deficiently realistic in their scientific conceptions". He then gave examples of incongruous and nonrational thoughts and actions now recognised as part of some neurotic reactions, and also entering into the thought processes of primitive peoples. He included such irrational actions as killing a rabid dog to prevent those bitten from developing rabies, and imagining that mind can be discussed without first distinguishing between mental and physical states. The oversolicitous mother, who refrains from washing the top of her baby's head, for fear that it should develop 'water on the brain'. Anointing a sword blade with a healing salve to cure a wound inflicted by it. Jackson linked dissimilar mental states, such as ordinary recollections with those of the *déjà vu* phenomena, and argued that erroneous projections in 'dreamy' states are analogous to the hallucinations of the insane.

Hughlings Jackson then gave several ludicrous examples of confusion of thoughts. An old woman remarked: "How lucky it is that Adam called all the animals by their right names. If he had called a lion a sheep, a butcher going to kill it for mutton would have been eaten himself". On his return from a voyage in the Red Sea, a sailor told his mother that he had seen flying fish. This she could not believe, but readily credited his claim to have drawn up a chariot wheel from the sea as she knew that Pharaoh's host had been engulfed there. An Irishman presented a cheque and when the cashier requested proof of his identity he produced a photograph of himself.

Finally, Hughlings Jackson was strongly opposed to crude popular materialism (as distinct from scientific materialism) as it created confusion by failing to distinguish between mental and nervous states. It is comparable, he believed, to stating that will can influence matter, and Jackson proceeded to ridicule these popular materialists in their own terms. If a man is unable to accept the proposition that hardness is real, he argued, then if he should hurt himself by walking into a lamp-post he should regard the pain as being in the post, and should rub not his head, but the lamp-post.

The 'Factors' of the Psychoses

Before discussing Hughlings Jackson's analysis of the functional psychoses, a current misconception concerning one of the alleged causes of 'insanity' should be considered. In Britain, David Skae (1863) and (1873) was among the first to suggest that a specific type of insanity is caused by onanism, and in a comprehensive review, Hare (1962) has shown that the 'insanity of masturbation', leading to dementia, was reflected in such current textbooks as those by Blandford (1871), Bucknill and Tuke (1874), Clouston (1883), and the first edition of Maudsley's *Pathology of Mind* (1879). Although most psychiatrists regarded masturbation as one cause of mental disorders, as early as 1875 Hughlings Jackson opposed this view, and in "Nervous symptoms in cases of congenital syphilis" (1875) wrote: "I do not, however, think it likely that it (masturbation) was a *cause* of the mental degradation in this case. I think it was rather the consequence. In all diseases affecting the mind, there is a reduction, not only to a lower intellectual level, but to a lower level of feeling, and in slight degrees there is seen to be only an apparent intensification of the inferior parts of the natural disposition. The vulgar man talks and acts offensively, the spiteful man becomes actively malicious, and the sensual man is openly indecent. I believe then that, as a rule, insane patients masturbate as a consequence of disease of the brain, and from the same cause that many of them become peevish and greedy . . . I would here remark that I do not believe masturbation causes epilepsy, or chorea, or any such symptoms, any more than I should believe it could cause paralysis of the *portio dura* nerve. It is sometimes replied to such a statement as this, that it is a 'question of fact'. It is not a question of fact with me, because I admit the fact, that is, I admit that many epileptics masturbate. All I deny is the inference that masturbation has caused their epilepsy". On this issue Hughlings Jackson was clearly better informed than his psychiatric colleagues, and it may have been one source of irritation to them.

In his discussion of the insanities as dissolutions Hughlings Jackson did not imply that there is necessarily a lesion of the brain itself, and Symonds (1960) has drawn attention to his belief that some mental disorders may be caused by a defect of the nutritional organs supplying the brain.

Hughlings Jackson's observations on the 'insanities' were based on his wide experience of post-ictal mental states, which provided him with an opportunity of studying psychiatric symptoms of a varied, yet distinct nature, and of establishing some degrees of correspondence between them, and the region of the brain affected. Insanity differs only in degree from epileptic mania, Jackson argued, as the insane also have a defect of consciousness analogous to loss of consciousness in epilepsy. The symptoms of insanity are caused, he believed, by the 'quasi-healthy actions' of the more automatic processes (I, 174). His interest in this relationship was stimulated by an observation of Bucknill and Tuke (1858), that six per cent of chronic epileptics are insane: he also quoted from Reynolds (1861) to the effect that seven per cent of 'nervous' diseases are caused by epilepsy. Jackson believed that epileptics whose fits come on suddenly with only a slight or no warning are most likely to become psychotic, but in this opinion he was opposed by one of the leading psychiatrists. "I do not agree with Hughlings Jackson that in cases of *petit mal* and slight convulsions", wrote Clouston in 1883, "the explosion, not finding vent in a motor form, is more apt to extend up into the mental centres".

Further, Hughlings Jackson broadened the diagnostic category of the 'insanities' beyond that generally accepted by psychiatrists, as is clear from this passage in "Remarks on dissolution of the nervous system" (1881), when seeking a unitary theory to explain them (II, 4–5): "We require for the science of insanity a rational generalisation, which shall show how insanities in the widest sense of the word, including not only cases specially described by alienists, but delirium in acute non-cerebral disease, degrees of drunkenness, and even sleep with dreaming are related to one another. Dreaming is for such purposes as important as any kind of insanity. More than this, we require a rational generalisation so wide as to show on the physical side relations of diseases of the mind, which are for physicians nothing but diseases of the highest centres, to all other diseases of the nervous system. We have to find some fundamental principle under which things so superficially different as the diseases empirically named hemiplegia, aphasia, acute mania, chorea, melancholia, permanent dementia, coma etc. can be methodically classified".

Hughlings Jackson attempted to solve this problem in "The factors of insanities" (1894), in which he put forward a neurological explanation of mental disorders. After subdividing the highest centres into four hypothetical layers, Jackson then applied evolutionary principles, as outlined earlier, in which a mental disorder reverses the evolutionary ascent. His first four factors governing the nature of the 'insanities' are: the different depths of dissolution; the type of person affected; its speed of action; the influences of local bodily states and external circumstances. After emphasizing the dual nature of a dissolution with negative and positive symptoms, Jackson amplified his precise meaning of a defect of consciousness accompanying all mental disorders in this footnote (II, 416–17n): "A patient in a lunatic asylum may write letters and occupy himself in other ways, may argue with his doctor about his own case with considerable pertinence. One does not say of such a patient that he has loss of consciousness, but that he has defect, slight defect, of consciousness. Moreover I think some insane patients' defect of consciousness is admitted in popular language when denied in technical terms. A patient may be said to be perfectly conscious, and yet be declared to be irresolute, forgetful, not clear in his observations, and apathetic. But this detailed statement grants that he is defective in will, memory, reason, and emotion, and since these are the (artificially distinguished) elements of consciousness, the statement amounts to saying that the patient has some degree of negative affection of consciousness (of object-consciousness). All this is consistent with his doing commonplace things definitely, with memory of all ordinary matters and of many long-past circumstances, with his talking to the point on simple things, and with his having some interest in striking occurrences; or, in other words, that with some defect of will, memory, reason, and emotion, there should be persistence of the rest of these so-called faculties — that with loss of 'some' mind or consciousness (with some defect of consciousness) there should be retention of the rest of mind or consciousness. For a man to be absolutely unconscious, or synonymously demented, is for him to have no will, no memory, no reason, and no emotion."

Jackson believed that the deeper the dissolution the lower is the range of evolution remaining, while the defect of consciousness is correspondingly greater. As the dissolution passes progressively deeper into Jackson's four hypothetical layers of the highest centres the remaining mentation becomes less elaborate until the fourth layer is reached, causing dementia, when only vital functions remain. He distinguished between primary and secondary delusions, both of them arising from activity of the intact layers. As an example of a secondary delusion Jackson mentioned a patient who believed she was about to be hanged. When she heard workmen hammering while making alterations in another ward it confirmed her belief that they were erecting a scaffold for her execution. Such a secondary delusion, Jackson argued, could not possibly be concomitant with the activities of diseased or paralysed nervous arrangements.

Jackson's second factor is the variation in the age, personality, and intelligence of the person affected. This raises the possibility of a link between epilepsy and mental disorders. In a historical review, Berrios (1979) states that Jackson regarded them as having a common cause, and quoted from Hughlings Jackson's "On temporary mental disorders after epileptic paroxysms" (1875). But as the title suggests, Jackson discussed only cases of 'epileptic insanity', and not other psychotic states. In "On the scientific and empirical investigation of epilepsies" (1874/6) he conceded that epilepsy may cause insanity in those individuals with an imperfectly developed higher and lower motor centre but essentially he believed that epilepsy and insanity are two completely separate conditions. "I do not believe that epilepsy and insanity have anything physiologically or pathologically in common", wrote Jackson (I, 230n) . . . "Epilepsy often causes insanity especially in those whose brain is imperfectly developed, but only, I think, as alcohol does, by damaging the brain. The cases of epilepsy in which mental infirmity follows are those in which the discharge begins in the very highest nervous arrangements — cases without 'a warning' or with a vague and general one". In "The factors of insanities" (1894), (II, 411-21) Jackson discussed the hereditary aspect of insanity and concluded that the condition is not transmitted as a cerebral lesion. Instead he regarded psychotic patients as inheriting a brain that is more likely to 'give out' under unfavourable conditions similar to those adversely affected by a relatively small quantity of alcohol.

His third factor is the rapidity of the dissolution. The more rapid it is then the more active is the remaining range of evolution. A patient with senile dementia, for example, undergoes a very slow dissolution, whereas one with post-ictal mania has a very rapid one.

The influence of local bodily states, and also of external circumstances, is Jackson's fourth factor. He argued that in health *muscae volitantes* form intra-ocular specks, but during a dissolution the subject may mistake them for rats or mice. He mentioned, too, that cramp in a sleeper's finger might be mistaken for a cat biting it. The patient's activities immediately before the dissolution influences the nature of the delusions. If, for example, a patient had been reading about kings, he might, after a dissolution, imagine himself to be a king.

In "On post-epileptic states" (1888) Jackson included another factor relating various types of 'insanities' to different areas of the brain. He thought, for example, that G.P.I. affects the frontal lobes and melancholia the posterior cortex. Hence he suggests that comparisons should be made between the physical conditions of various 'insanities' and different degrees of the same insanity. He also recommended a comparison with such lower-level lesions as those causing aphasia and hemiplegia. Each factor, he thought, should be related to others so that in every mental disorder there is an interaction of five variables. "I deal with mental symptoms", he wrote (I, 382), "as signs only of what is not going on or of what is going on wrongly in the nervous system". Finally he compared different degrees of the 'insanities' to various post-ictal phenomena.

As first pointed out by Critchley (1960), Hughlings Jackson's 'factors' might well be applied to any neurological disease; and the limitations of his purely neurological explanation of mental disorders have been criticised by Lord Brain (1963). By strictly separating physical events from psychical ones, Lord Brain argues that, when mind is disordered by a lesion of the nervous system, a neurological disorder is discernible, actually or potentially, either by the abnormal neurochemistry, or through neuropathological changes. But when mind is disordered as a reaction to the individual's previous experience, a physical explanation is not possible. Hemiplegia, delirium, and coma are states of body or mind which may be attributed to a physical disorder of the nervous system. The major psychoses may also be found to have an organic cause, in which event, they may, too, be described in physical terms. Psychogenic disorders, on the other hand, belong to a different causative category, and cannot be described, as Jackson attempted, in neurological terms, but only in psychological terms. Temkin (1971), who also regards Jackson's neurological explanations as 'speculative', points out that his evolutionary functional levels, and his hypothetical subdivision of the highest centres, are schematic entities rather than anatomical or functional realities. Hence he concludes that Jackson's theory of the 'insanities' rests on "philosophical views which had their limitations in the 19th century". Finally, Philip Evans (1972) has rightly described Jackson's theory as being "too mechanistic" to be fully exploitable in psychiatry. Nevertheless, Jackson did make significant contributions to psychiatry by his discussion of mental disorders as regressions with a defect of consciousness; and Lassek (1970) considers that his concept of psychiatric symptoms as release phenomena is "one of the most original".

Hughlings Jackson and the Genesis of Temporal Lobe Epilepsy

Among others, Temkin (1971), and Taylor and Marsh (1980), have shown that what later became known as temporal lobe epilepsy had been described long before Hughlings Jackson began his observations. Nevertheless, Jackson and his colleague James Anderson (1887) were the first to record the association between a pathological disturbance in the mesial temporal region, the 'dreamy' state, and psychomotor automatisms, often accompanied by olfactory or gustatory hallucinations. With his customary generosity, Jackson repeatedly pointed out that his observations had benefited from David Ferrier's earlier description of a gustatory centre in the lower extremity of the temporo-sphenoidal lobe, where stimulation in the cat and monkey provoked movements of the lips, tongue, cheek pouches, or jaws. But Sir William Gowers recognised Jackson's originality in his lecture "On special senses discharges from organic disease" (1909), in which he stated "that facts are rare, and those already gathered have been made to yield their lessons by the Master himself, beyond whom we cannot hope to go".

Jackson's description of 'uncinate' epilepsy evolved from his study of the aurae of the special senses, and were made during two distinct periods. Between 1866 and 1888 he

collected sporadic, and somewhat isolated, items of information which had some subsequent relevance to temporal
lobe epilepsy. During the second phase from 1888 to 1899
Hughlings Jackson brought together these observations, and
demonstrated the clinico-pathological correlation of 'dreamy'
states with behavioural automatisms in 'uncinate' epilepsy.

According to Gowers, Jackson's first observations appeared
in "Clinical remarks on the occasional occurrence of subjective
sensations of smell in patients who are liable to epileptiform
seizures, or who have symptoms of mental derangement, and
in others" (1866). Here he suggested that the association of
olfactory hallucinations and mental deterioration was probably caused by an embolus of the anterior cerebral artery.
A year later in "Remarks on disorderly movements of chorea
and convulsions" (1867) Jackson regarded epileptic mania as
a manifestation of the epileptic discharge. But he radically
changed his opinion in "Remarks on the double condition of
loss of consciousness and mental automatism following certain
epileptic seizures" (1873) and instead stated that the discharge causes only the negative symptom of loss of consciousness, whereas automatisms represent the positive release
symptoms. Henceforth he discussed epilepsy as a "reduction
to a more automatic mental state" in which 'dreamy' states
represent a slight reduction while epileptic mania and coma
are greater ones. Jackson compared them to other 'reductions'
in dreaming and drunkenness.

In a lecture given at the Wakefield Asylum "On temporary
mental disorders after epileptic paroxysms" (1875), (I, 119–
34), Hughlings Jackson vividly likened mental automatisms
to 'epileptic dreams'. He rejected Falret's notion of 'masked'
epilepsy in which a manic outburst, or some other psychological event, replaces a fit. Instead Jackson explained them
in terms of the removal of higher control permitting increased
automatic actions. Of the many cases he related, one concerned a violent postman whose unruly behaviour subsided
as soon as he was given his post-bag; and a clerk who

unconsciously ate his dinner and returned to the restaurant to enquire whether he had paid for it. A traveller had a post-ictal automatism at Blackfriars, and walked about two miles to the 'Elephant and Castle' before he came round. Of particular interest was the man who unconsciously went into his kitchen where he was found "mixing cocoa in a dirty gallipot, half filled with bread and milk intended for the cat, and stirring the mixture with a mustard spoon" . . . (I, 126). Subsequently Jackson realised that he had overlooked the association with a 'dreamy' state of this unconscious performance of elaborate actions.

Hughlings Jackson first regarded 'dreamy' states as 'mental diplopia', or states of 'double consciousness', and in "Remarks on evolution and dissolution of the nervous system" (1887) (II, 88n) he stated that they represent the remains of consciousness of present surroundings (remains of object consciousness) combined with increased consciousness of some former surroundings or increased subject consciousness. Later he was less certain about this explanation, and, in "On post-epileptic states" (1888/9) confessed that he now felt "uncertain as to the exact symptomatological nature of 'dreamy' states" (I, 380).

When discussing aurae in "Remarks on systemic sensations in epilepsies" (1874), Jackson regarded their order of frequency as being those of sight, smell, and hearing: he believed that warnings of taste are "very rare" whereas epigastric sensations are the commonest, often accompanied by feelings of fear, which one patient termed "an indescribable feeling of horror". He defined fear as "anger broken down", and considered it to be a manifestation of the effects of the discharge (II, 88n). From his casebook, Jackson gave extracts of his patients' own 'reminiscences' in "Intellectual warnings of epileptic seizures" (1876), (I, 274–5), which include: "old scenes revert", "I feel in some strange place", "a dreamy state"; "a panorama of something familiar yet strange" and "Oh, I saw that before!" were among other phrases used.

One patient described his experience as "if I were to have a fit, and see the fender, I should say, Dear me, I saw that fender before!" A highly intelligent patient felt that he was in a state of 'double consciousness', which Jackson regarded as an accurate description, as he believed that in such states there is diminished object consciousness and increased subject consciousness. He agreed that some healthy people have similar experiences but they are not, however, a prelude to an epileptic paroxysm, and, in any event, these healthy individuals have insight into the nature of their experiences. In his next paper on the subject, "Lectures on the diagnosis of epilepsy" (1879), Jackson made a clear distinction between an aura and a 'dreamy' state in this passage (I, 295n): "In no case do I believe it possible that *elaborate* states ('dreamy' states, 'actions', or 'movements') can occur from an *epileptic* discharge. I believe all *elaborate* positive states occur from, or arise during, an increased energising of centres permitted by removal of control of higher centres". Hence Jackson preferred "'dreamy state" to "intellectual aura" as he did not regard these experiences as comparable to visual or olfactory warnings. In "On right- or left-sided spasm at the onset of epileptic paroxysms, and on crude sensations, warnings and elaborate mental states" (1880/1), (I, 313), Jackson mentioned that "it would be a remarkably well directed and distributed epileptic discharge which would give rise to the exceedingly compound mental state of being somewhere else. Besides . . . it is scarcely likely that one thing, an epileptic discharge, should be the physical condition of a sudden stench in the nose — a crude sensation — and also the physical condition of an infinitely more elaborate psychical state". After distinguishing between excitatory and release phenomena with an aura arising from the former, and a 'dreamy' state from the latter, Jackson recommended that all patients with 'dreamy' states should be fully investigated for epilepsy. He first mentioned a link between 'dreamy' states and behavioural automatisms in "Psychology and the nervous system" (1879), and "hoped sometime to be able to show that actions in these cases are in accord with the 'dreamy' state". As an example, he mentioned a patient in a 'dreamy' state who felt that he was 'somewhere else' and whose father noticed that he always tried to escape by 'making for the door'.

Hughlings Jackson had now studied fourteen patients with 'dreamy' states, and analysed the symptoms, in the third of his "Lectures on the diagnosis of epilepsy" (1879). He believed that, hitherto, the condition had attracted "little attention in this country", although it had been well described in France by Falret, Voisin, and others. Jackson came to regard the 'dreamy' state as a 'double mental state' with a negative defect, or loss of consciousness, associated with a positive 'dreamy' state, well illustrated in one patient who felt that the normal activities of his mind had ceased, but simultaneously "I seem to think of a thousand different things all in a moment." If he then lost consciousness the 'dreamy' state would vanish. When patients have automatisms but no 'dreamy' state Jackson called this 'epileptic somnambulism'. He then drew a distinction between 'dreamy' states without actions and unremembered automatisms, which he subdivided into five groups corresponding to the degree of behaviour disorder. The sequence of events in 'dreamy' states accompanied by automatisms is first a state of 'double consciousness' with a negative defect of consciousness, and a positive 'dreamy' state. Deepening unconsciousness is accompanied by automatisms, and on recovery the patient only remembers fragments of his 'dreamy' state. Jackson then studied sensory warnings in relation to 'dreamy' states, with or without actions, beginning with epigastric sensations often accompanied by fear. He then queried whether there was a relationship between auditory hallucinations, coloured vision, 'dreamy' states, and gustatory hallucinations. "We should, I think, see whether or not there may be in some cases intelligible relations betwixt the states", he wrote (I, 305–6), "(1) warning; (2) 'dreamy' state of less elaborate stage; (3) actions after loss of consciousness and the emotional form of the conduct". In a penetrating analysis of 'dreamy' states and reminiscences in "On right- or left-sided spasm at the onset of epileptic paroxysms etc." (1880/1), Jackson found that they occurred more frequently in association with lesions of the non-dominant hemisphere. He mentioned that he had never encountered an objective emotion of anger, but noticed that when "fear occurs at the onset of a paroxysm with or without an epigastric sensation the first spasm is on the left" (I, 316).

Another aspect of the syndrome he was trying to formulate was the site of the lesion giving rise to a 'dreamy' state heralded by warnings of smell or taste. The answer was provided by Jackson's colleague James Anderson in "On sensory epilepsy. A case of basal cerebral tumour affecting the left temporo-sphenoidal lobe, and giving rise to a paroxysmal taste-sensation and 'dreamy' state" (1887). During the early stages of his illness, when the patient was under Hughlings Jackson's care, he experienced 'dreamy' states involving scenes of reversions to childhood. Later he had auditory hallucinations together with a "rough bitter sensation in his mouth" followed by a feeling of something passing over his arm, shoulder and the "back of the brain". At necropsy a tumour was found in the uncinate region, which Jackson considered to be the first occasion that a 'dreamy' state had been associated with a brain lesion.

Undoubtedly Anderson's case stimulated Hughlings Jackson's own observations, as two years later he had notes on fifty patients with 'dreamy' states, and suggested that empirically they should be grouped together as "a particular variety of epilepsy". He mentioned, too, that his earlier contributions had "attracted little attention", and after stressing the serious implications of 'dreamy' states associated with tasting, chewing, or spitting movements, confessed "that in former years I have under-rated, and even, I found, neglected the 'dreamy' state" (I, 390). As an example, he mentioned his earliest case report of elaborate behavioural automatisms in a man who unconsciously mixed cocoa with the cat's food and added that he had omitted to mention that the paroxysm was preceded by a "sort of 'dreamy' state coming on suddenly". Among Jackson's five case reports was a patient with an olfactory aura, 'dreamy' state, and bilateral papilloedema, relieved by mercurial inunctions, and although necropsy was refused, he confidently predicted a syphilitic gumma in the right temporal lobe.

Although Hughlings Jackson now had information on many aspects of temporal lobe epilepsy, it was not until 1889 that one of his own patients came to necropsy. She was Eliza Joad, whose 'dreamy' state, and inability to recognise persons, objects, and places was combined with visual hallucinations of a little black woman engaged in cooking. She described her olfactory hallucinations as like the smell of "burning dirty stuff". At necropsy a large sarcoma was found involving the right temporo-sphenoidal lobe with smaller growth in the right hippocampus. In 1898 another of Jackson's patients with 'dreamy' states, automatisms, and tasting movements came to necropsy; but, as this case is of particular interest, it will be discussed separately.

Hughlings Jackson first began to use the term 'uncinate group of fits' in a contribution to the *Lancet*: "On asphyxia in slight epileptic paroxysms. On the symptomatology of slight epileptic fits supposed to depend on discharge-lesions of the uncinate gyrus" (1899). In the same year he published another fatal case of a 'dreamy' state accompanied by a sensation of smell, and although necropsy was refused he confidently diagnosed a tumour of the right temporo-sphenoidal lobe. He went on to review the post-mortem findings in other cases, and evolved the diagnostic category of the 'uncinate group of epileptic fits', which is well summarised in this passage (I, 467): ". . . The discharge lesions in these cases are made up of some cells, not of the uncinate group along, but of some cells of different parts of a region of which this gyrus is part — a very vague circumscription, I admit — the uncinate region. In cases of this group there is at the onset of the paroxysms a crude sensation of smell or one of taste, or there are movements of chewing, smacking of the lips, etc. (sometimes there is spitting). In some cases of this group there is a warning by what is known as the epigastric sensation, a crude development of a systemic sensation; this warning sometimes occurs along with a crude sensation of smell or with the chewing etc. movements. Different varieties of this group of cases, depend, I suppose, on discharge lesions of different parts of what I call the uncinate region. As will have been inferred, it is supposed that especially in this cortical region, not confined to this region, are the physical bases of some of the systemic sensations — the physical bases of these systemic sensations which, to speak very roughly, especially appertain to the digestive system.

"Many of the symptoms of even slight paroxysms of uncinate fits depend, of course, on discharges widespread beyond, some far beyond, the uncinate region — depend on discharges *secondary* to the *primary* discharge, that of the discharge lesion". Sir Charles Symonds (1954) has emphasised that Hughlings Jackson did not restrict 'uncinate' fits to lesions in the uncinate gyrus. On the contrary he considered that they may arise from discharging cells in various parts of a region of which the uncinate gyrus forms part. "Much time has been lost during recent years", wrote Jasper (1958), "by the failure to recognise" Hughlings Jackson's pioneering studies on 'uncinate' epilepsy. He mentioned, too, that 'dreamy' states do not always accompany uncinate fits and, in some instances, they may be associated with crude auditory sensations instead. Jackson's clinical observations correlated with his post-mortem findings of a focal lesion "approximate" (according to Bailey (1958)) "to our notions of temporal lobe seizures"; and Hill (1981) considers that his observations have been fully vindicated in the present diagnosis of temporal lobe epilepsy. Hughlings Jackson's automatisms have been more precisely redefined by Fenton (1975). He regarded them as "a state of clouding of consciousness which occurs during or immediately after a seizure . . . when . . . the individual retains control of posture and muscle tone but performs simple or complex movements and actions without being aware of what is happening".

After Jackson's retirement his former assistant, Sir William Gowers, extended his observations, and included a 37-year-old patient with an aura of smell, papilloedema, and tenderness over the right temporal region, on whom Victor Horsley operated but was unable to remove an infiltrating glioma. When discussing brain disease presenting with auditory hallucinations, Gowers (1909) included one patient first treated by Hughlings Jackson, "who with characteristic kindness, has placed the notes at my disposal". He had a history of syphilis, hallucinations of a peal of bells, and at necropsy a gumma was found in the right temporal lobe. But Jackson's last house physician, S. A. Kinnier Wilson (1928), disagreed with his former chief, and argued that from a phenomenological viewpoint, it was of no consequence as to whether 'dreamy' states represented excitation or release phenomena. But he did support Jackson in stressing the localising significance of aurae, and modified his dictum that "there are as many different epilepsies as there are different warnings" to "different epilepsies each have their own warning and some have no warning". Kinnier Wilson distinguished four types of 'dreamy' states: the familiarity or *déjà vu* type, the unfamiliarity or unreality type, the panoramic memory type, and the incomplete or abortive type. Without actually separating them into categories Hughlings Jackson had, in fact, delineated similar types.

'Uncinate' epilepsy was subsequently combined with 'epileptic equivalents' or 'psychical seizures', and termed 'psychomotor' epilepsy by Gibbs, Gibbs, and Lennox (1937) (1938) and (1938), although Hill (1981) states that 'psychomotor' was first used by Van Gieson (1924). The site of the lesion was not, at first, recognised until Gibbs, Gibbs, and Fuster (1948) demonstrated foci of spike potentials in one or both anterior temporal lobes in nearly all patients, and shortly afterwards Hughlings Jackson's 'uncinate' epilepsy became known as temporal lobe epilepsy (Penfield, 1954; Symonds 1954; Hill 1963; Driver 1970; Falconer and Taylor 1970). The concept of temporal lobe epilepsy has been summarised by Gaustaut (1953) and De Jong (1957). Although all psychomotor seizures arise from a discharge in the temporal lobe, not all patients with temporal lobe epilepsy have psychomotor attacks.

Hughlings Jackson's 'uncinate fits' with psychomotor automatisms were confirmed by Feindel and Penfield (1954) in a series of 155 patients operated on for temporal lobe epilepsy. They found that 121 of them (78%) had attacks characterised by various behavioural automatisms, and concluded that temporal lobe seizures with behavioural automatisms "more closely correspond as regards both the seizure pattern and the site of the pathological lesion, to the uncinate fits as described by Hughlings Jackson". But Jackson never managed to complete his proposed observations into the emotional experiences of patients with temporal lobe epilepsy, which was undertaken on one hundred patients nearly a century later by Denis Williams (1956). He found that 61 experienced fear, 21 were depressed, while 9 had pleasant, and a similar number had unpleasant experiences. Fear predominated when the disturbance involved the anterior half of either temporal lobe, and was present in 70% of 50 patients with an anterior temporal focus. Depression was found in diffuse lesions, while pleasure and its opposite were mainly associated with posterior temporal lobe lesions. Williams concludes that the elucidation of the cerebral physiology of emotion "has topical importance on account of the expansion of empirical physical methods of treatment in psychiatry".

'Psychic' or 'experiential' manifestations of temporal lobe seizures may be divided into perceptual, emotional, or

mnemonic categories. The last mentioned includes disturbances of memory and recall together with illusions or hallucinations of familiarity or unfamiliarity such as *déjà vu* or
jamais vu. By stimulation through stereotaxically implanted
electrodes, Gloor, Olivier, and Quesney (1981) found that
the limbic structures, particularly the amygdala, were predominantly involved in 'experiential' manifestations rather
than the neo-temporal cortex.

A link between epilepsy and psychosis has been explored
historically by Berrios (1979). The increased probability of
psychotic states in temporal lobe epilepsy has been shown by
Bartlet (1957), Pond (1957), and Dongier (1960), while Beard
and Slater (1962) and Slater, Beard, and Glithero (1963) have
described a schizophrenia-like psychosis of epilepsy. Although
this condition resembles schizophrenia, there is no genetic
predisposition; affect is usually appropriate and it is not
accompanied by a similar degree of deterioration. Further,
this relation between epilepsy and psychosis occurs with a
much greater frequency than by chance expectation. In a
retrospective study of 50 randomly selected patients with
temporal lobe epilepsy Flor-Henry (1969) confirmed most
of the findings of Slater *et al.* and found a diminished frequency of epileptic seizures during the psychosis. Flor-Henry
considers that a schizophrenia-like psychosis is more likely to
arise in association with epilepsy of the dominant temporal
lobe whereas manic-depressive psychosis is associated with a
lesion in the non-dominant hemisphere. Bear and Fedio
(1977) devised a rating scale comparing fifteen patients with
right temporal lobe abnormalities with twelve patients with
left temporal lobe lesions. Those with right-sided lesions were
rated higher for an elated mood whereas patients with left-
sided lesions scored higher for anger, paranoia, and dependence.

The relation between epilepsy and psychiatric disturbances
has been classified into peri-ictal and inter-ictal. Peri-ictal pro-
dromata include disturbances of affect, particularly increased

irritability; while psychic events in temporal lobe epilepsy include virtually all the manifestations described in patients with schizophrenia. Inter- or post-ictal psychiatric disturbances include automatism, disturbances in consciousness, and other behaviour changes such as pallor, lip-smacking, chewing, swallowing, muttering, and blinking. In general, psychotic disturbances in patients with temporal lobe epilepsy are predominantly of a paranoid nature.

Over a hundred years after Hughlings Jackson's pioneering observations, a group of London Hospital consultants have accumulated information on one of the largest series of patients with temporal lobe epilepsy. In 666 patients, Currie, Heathfield, Henson, and Scott (1971) have shown that the average age of onset is 28 years; that loss of consciousness occurs in 77% (57% having *grand mal* seizures) and 51% have psychomotor attacks. In only one-quarter could a cause be detected, and of these 9.5% had a tumour, mostly gliomas, while 7% had suffered a significant head injury. Other possible factors include a history of an abnormal birth 7%; 11% had a family history of epilepsy, and 5% had infantile seizures.

It is now recognized that an equivalent clinical pattern may be produced by an epileptic focus in areas of the brain other than the temporal lobe. Hence in the new classification by the International League against Epilepsy psychomotor and temporal lobe epilepsy have been supplanted by the term 'complex-partial seizures'. Despite this reclassification Feindel (1974) has rightly suggested that though the eponym 'Jacksonian' is reserved for focal sensori-motor attacks, it could equally well be justified in the description of temporal lobe seizures with automatisms.

The Case of Dr. Z.

In the May issue of *The Practitioner* (1874) a short article entitled "A prognostic and therapeutic indication in epilepsy" appeared under the pseudonym of "Quaerens". The anonymous contributor wrote that "last year I had the misfortune to become for the first time in my life subject to occasional epilepsy". After giving brief examples of *déjà vu* experiences from the writings of Dickens, Coleridge, and Tennyson, "Quaerens" stated that he had experienced such feelings of 'recollection' since boyhood, although they became more frequent during a period of over-work immediately before his first *grand mal* seizure. On two later occasions, he had noticed an association between the frequency and intensity of his 'reminiscences', and the onset of *grand mal* fits. "Quaerens" then made two points: first, though literary men referred to the universality of the *déjà vu* phenomena, he believed that such experiences are symptoms of epilepsy, and that efforts should be made to abort the subsequent onset of *grand mal*. Secondly, he suggested that the association between 'recollections' and *petit mal* should be investigated. Hughlings Jackson noticed this contribution, and "Quaerens" eventually came under his care.

At this stage some confusion about dates should be resolved. In 1881 Hughlings Jackson gave the date of publication of "Quaerens's" paper as 1870, and corrected it to 1874 seven years later. In "On a particular variety of epilepsy ('intellectual aura')" (1888) Jackson published a long account of "Quaerens's" illness, much of it in his own words, and stated that he had first been consulted in February 1880. But under the pseudonym of "Dr Z." he gave another case report of an epileptic doctor in a "Case of epilepsy with tasting movements etc." (1898) where he mentioned that he had first met him in December 1877 when "Z." was 26 years old. Thornton (1976) was the first to point out that "Quaerens" and "Dr Z." were the same person. This is confirmed by Jackson's reference to the onset of "Dr Z.'s" epilepsy which he initially "regarded . . . as of no practical importance". These, and other sentences, are the exact words used earlier by "Quaerens". Differences in the dates may be explained by the fact that Jackson referred to their first meeting in 1877, but he did not begin to treat him until three years later.

In an interesting study of historical detection Taylor and Marsh (1980) have uncovered the identity of "Quaerens", or "Dr Z.", and in so doing, have not only revealed a dramatic and poignant episode in the Victorian medical scene, but they have also widened our knowledge of the background to Hughlings Jackson's formulation of 'uncinate' fits. The patient was Arthur Thomas Myers, M.A., M.D., F.R.C.P., born in 1851 into an intellectually distinguished family, whose father was incumbent of St John's Church, Keswick. A notable sportsman in his youth, Arthur Myers played cricket for Cheltenham College; he took part in the public schools rackets match; and at Trinity College, Cambridge was captain of cricket, and gained a half-blue in tennis. Myers was a 22-year-old undergraduate when he gave this account of his first *petit mal* experience: "I first noticed symptoms which I subsequently learnt to describe as *petit mal* when living at one of our universities in 1871. I was in very good health, and know of no temporary disturbing causes. I was waiting at the front of the College staircase, in the open air, for a friend. I was carelessly looking around me watching people passing etc, when my attention was suddenly absorbed in my own mental state, of which I know no more than that it seemed to me to be a vivid and unexpected 'recollection'; — of what, I do not know. My friend found me a minute or two later, leaning my back against the wall, looking rather pale, and feeling puzzled and stupid for the moment. In another minute or two I felt quite normal again, and was as much amused as my friend at finding that I could give no distinct account of what had happened, or what I had 'recollected'".

Two years later, despite his disability, Arthur Myers took a first in classics, and subsequently a second-class honours degree in the natural sciences. When he wrote to *The Practitioner*, he was a medical student at St George's Hospital where he qualified L.S.A. in 1879. Myers then proceeded M.D. (Cantab.) in 1881; gained his M.R.C.P. a year later, and was house physician, and later registrar, at St George's Hospital, where he developed a system of indexing case records. During his hospital practice Myers became friendly with Dr Frederick Dawtrey Drewitt (1848–1942), an erudite physician of catholic interests who was three years his senior. Educated at Winchester and Christ Church, Oxford, Dawtrey Drewitt later held house appointments at the Hospital for Sick Children, and at the Belgrave Hospital for Children, where he probably used his influence to get Arthur Myers appointed to the honorary staff. Among Myers's earliest medical contributions were several conventional clinical observations including one on Raynaud's disease (1885), another on the chronic nervous sequelae of smallpox (1886) and he wrote to *Nature* on medical indexing and cataloguing (1886/7). Undoubtedly his most significant contribution was his anonymous six-page account of his epilepsy included in Hughlings Jackson's "A particular variety of epilepsy" (1888). By 1880 Myers had suffered eighteen *grand mal* seizures, and "many hundreds" of attacks of *petit mal* accompanied by elaborate *déjà vu* feelings, occasional psychomotor automatisms, followed by amnesia. The only local symptom that Jackson elicited was a tingling in the right hand. Observers had reported that Myers went pale; his facial expression became vacant, and he made distinctly smacking movements of the tongue, like tasting movements, accompanied by a slight movement of the lower jaw. There were no hallucinations of sight, sound, taste, smell, or feeling. Myers was rather vague about the frequency of his *grand mal* fits but estimated that they occurred at long intervals of "as much as eighteen months". During 1887 he noticed that his attacks of *petit mal* were accompanied by less vivid *déjà vu* feelings, although he experienced several complex automatisms followed by long periods of amnesia, some lasting fifteen minutes. Among several examples he gave was one *petit mal* attack which came on as he was taking out his stethoscope to examine a young patient with a chest infection. Myers turned away to avoid entering into a conversation, and next recalled that he was sitting at a writing table in an empty room with no patient in sight. An hour later, he noticed the patient in a ward bed, and on looking up his case notes, found that he had recorded a diagnosis of "pneumonia of the left base". He discovered indirectly that he had made a full physical examination, written out a diagnosis, and advised admission. When he re-examined the patient, he was relieved to find that his conscious diagnosis was the same as his unremembered one. On several occasions these *petit mal* seizures passed unnoticed during ward rounds.

While Hughlings Jackson was monitoring Arthur Myers's neurological symptoms, his brilliant and erratic brother Frederic Myers was closely following his psychical experiences as they confirmed his theory of 'double consciousness' of the subliminal and supraliminal selves. F. W. H. Myers believed that the subliminal self was concerned with thoughts, feelings, and past experiences concealed beneath the normal threshold of consciousness as distinct from the supraliminal self situated above this level. It was probably at Arthur's suggestion that Frederic explained the actions and perceptions of the supraliminal self in terms of a Jacksonian hierarchical arrangement of nervous centres. But Frederic Myers believed that the unconscious subliminal part had a greater range of mentation than the supraliminal self embracing regressive, creative, and 'mythopoetic' (a tendency to weave fantasies) functions. He even explained the inspiration of genius as a kind of Dionysian 'subliminal uprush' introducing brilliant and profound ideas into the consciousness.

F. W. H. Myers (1843–1903), who had been a prodigious scholar at Cheltenham and Trinity College, Cambridge, described himself as a man of "sensuous and emotional temperament", which he expressed in his early volumes of poems. On his own admission, too, he was given to "acts of swaggering folly" in that he claimed to be the first Englishman to swim across the Niagara pool just below the falls alone at night. Elected to a fellowship as a classics lecturer at Trinity College, Myers resigned in 1869, in order to help Henry Sidgwick organise the movement for higher education for women; and in 1872 was appointed Inspector of Schools. Classical scholar, poet, essayist, and champion of women's higher education, Myers moved easily in the highest social and literary circles of Victorian London and amongst his close friends were the Duke of Albany and Professor William James.

Since 1870 Myers had been interested in mesmerism, spiritualism, multiple personality, automatic writing, and other imperfectly explored phenomena. And with Professor Henry Sidgwick, Edmund Gurney, Frank Podmore, and other friends, F. W. H. Myers was one of the founders of the Society for Psychical Research, whose objective was to investigate "that large group of debateable phenomena designated by such terms as mesmeric, psychical and Spiritualistic". Myers was primarily interested in investigating survival after death, but before attempting to communicate with the spirits of the departed, he undertook an objective study into various parapsychological phenomena. And in these investigations Arthur Myers's medical knowledge was invaluable.

Through their survey of family letters, Taylor and Marsh (1980) have shown that Frederic and Arthur Myers were closely attached, and the doctor now began to share his brother's interest in psychical research. In 1886 they went to Le Havre to witness Pierre Janet's experiment of hypnotising at a distance a subject "Léonie", the success of which the Myers brothers regarded as confirmation of the phenomenon of telepathy. After hypnotic suggestions given at a distance the subject responded successfully in nineteen out of twenty-five experiments. The Myers brothers were impressed. And in May 1886 they jointely presented a paper on their obser-vations to the Société de Psychologie Physiologique. In the same year Edmund Gurney, F. W. H. Myers, and Frank Podmore published their classic work on parapsychology, *Phantasms of the Living.* Herein they stated that telepathy could be demonstrated experimentally, and claimed that impressions of persons undergoing a severe crisis, such as death, might be perceived by others with a frequency that could not be explained by chance. In his discussion of hallu-cinations Gurney found that a great number occurred in healthy people, which contradicted the current notion that they are necessarily manifestations of insanity, weakness of intellect, or gullibility. In 1889 Arthur Myers was a member of the committee directed by Professor Sidgwick to extend Gurney's enquiries. Although this committee was unable to explain the majority of hallucinations occurring in the healthy they did find that some subjects had a predisposition to externalise figures or sounds which they called "an idiosyn-cratic central hyperaesthesia", and likened the experience to vivid dreams. They found, too, that a small number of sub-jects were undergoing grief or anxiety. Arthur Myers also took part in telepathic experiments on the thought-transference of numbers, and contributed about a dozen articles on aspects of parapsychology to various psychical research publications. Hypnosis was one of his major interests on which he wrote a section in Hack Tuke's *Dictionary of Psychological*

Medicine, and a biographical note on Esdaile to the *Dictionary of National Biography*.

But Arthur Myers's writings and medical practice were undertaken against a background of frequent fits accompanied by behavioural automatisms and succeeded by lengthy periods of amnesia. Hughlings Jackson actually witnessed two of his epileptic attacks. One occurred at a meeting of a medical society when Myers suddenly stopped talking, and made barely audible smacking movements. Another happened in Hughlings Jackson's consulting room when Myers abruptly terminated his conversation; then bent forward over one, and the other, arm of the chair, and felt on the floor as if searching for something. He then picked up a pin and jokingly threatened to prick Jackson with it. As they lived in identical houses next door to one another, Jackson discussed with Myers the possibility of utilising a third room on the ground floor. Although Myers carried on a perfectly rational conversation he was unable to recall any of it the next day. On another occasion, while in a post-ictal state, Myers had indulged in some form of anti-social behaviour, regarded by Jackson as "criminal" as it "could have led to very serious consequences had not, fortunately, his condition been known and overlooked by those concerned". Hughlings Jackson gave several examples from Myers's clinical notes, written when his concentration was shattered by a fit and he composed such unintelligible word salads as: "For the last 18 mos years there has been some decided indefinite on R. side in dress circle". But despite his disability Arthur Myers continued to write the occasional article and was still able to attend his patients. His "Hypnotism at home and abroad" appeared in the *Practitioner* (1890); and in collaboration with Frederic their "Mind-cure, faith-cure and the miracle of Lourdes" was published in the *Proceedings of the Society for Psychical Research* (1893). It revealed their robustly sceptical attitude towards miracles and other occult phenomena. After objectively deflating some of the more dubious aspects of the

Lourdes 'miracles' they likened the spurious pretensions of Mary Baker Eddy's 'Christian Scientists' to "the chariots and trumpets of the itinerant quack".

But by 1893, when Arthur Myers was elected F.R.C.P., he was ironically no longer fit to practise medicine. Throughout his long illness he had received the constant help and support of Dawtrey Drewitt, then physician to the West London Hospital, and on Myers's premature retirement they shared the tenancy of No. 2 Manchester Square next door to Hughlings Jackson. This was an acceptable and convenient means of managing a patient with a chronic mental illness, as the two physicians were close friends with sufficient means to maintain a large household. Unfortunately their joint tenancy was short as *The Times* of the 13th January 1894 reported the death of Arthur Myers at the age of 42. Dawtrey Drewitt, having been called by a servant, found him unconscious and despite the maintenance of continuous artificial respiration by six doctors for thirty-two hours he never regained consciousness. Myers's background, and the circumstances of his death, raised the possibility of suicide. He was unmarried; he was suffering from an intractable illness; he had retired prematurely, and for many years had been in the habit of relieving his insomnia by taking increasingly larger doses of chloral. Further, Taylor and Marsh have shown that two persons close to him had probably committed suicide. The first was his cousin Annie, whose two sisters had died insane, while she herself was married to a manic-depressive husband who required frequent institutional care. Annie and Frederic Myers had indulged in a passionate "love affair of the spirit", and in his privately circulated "Fragments of Inner Life", Frederic Myers claimed that they had been engaged in a passionate platonic love affair during a prior existence, and would be reunited after death. On the 1st September 1876, after trying unsuccessfully to slash her throat with a pair of scissors, Annie drowned herself in Ullswater. Frederic and Arthur heard of her unexplained suicide while on holiday in Scandinavia.

The other likely suicide was that of Edmund Gurney, friend and patient of Arthur Myers, for whom the latter had been in the habit of prescribing chloral and belladonna to relieve trigeminal neuralgia. Recently Myers had changed to giving small doses of chloroform as an analgesic. Gurney was found dead in a hotel bedroom in Brighton from an overdose of chloroform, while attending a meeting of the Society for Psychical Research. At the inquest Arthur Myers gave evidence concerning his treatment, but through lack of information on the deceased's state of mind at the material time, the jury returned a verdict of accidental death. The circumstances of Myers's own death were rather similar to those of Gurney's. And if Arthur Myers shared his brother's belief in life after death, and there is every reason to believe that he did, would it not be preferable to terminate his shattered twilight existence for the possibility of a more wholesome one hereafter?

Necropsy was undertaken by Dr. Walter Colman, whom Hughlings Jackson "begged . . . to call on me before . . . in order to ask him to search the taste region of Ferrier on each half of the brain very carefully". His request was promted by a history of tasting movements, and also from Jackson's detailed enquiries as to whether Myers had noticed any subjective localising signs. Although he could not be sure, Myers had indicated on 'very scanty' evidence that the right side of his face was slightly more affected than the left.

When he began the necropsy, allegedly thirty hours after death, Colman found extreme post-mortem lividity, and advanced decomposition, and noted that the weather was warm and damp. On dissecting the brain a very small area of softening was found in the left uncinate gyrus, which on sectioning revealed "a small cavity 5/8th inch below the surface just in front of the recurved tip of the uncus". Unfortunately, the brain was too soft and friable to allow Colman to prepare microscopic sections. Taylor and Marsh have cast slight doubt on Colman's post-mortem findings, although Hughlings Jackson, Dawtrey Drewitt, James Taylor, and Guy

Wood were also present. They do, however, concede that a lesion in the left uncinate area was "very likely", and suggest the possibility of either a hamartoma, or more likely, focal dysplasia. Whatever its nature there was, undoubtedly, an uncinate lesion as Hughlings Jackson's strict regard for truth was such that it would have been quite impossible for him to 'invent' one to confirm his clinical suppositions.

At the inquest, held on the 15th January 1894, it was legally determined that Arthur Thomas Myers did not commit suicide. Mr. Ernest Myers, barrister-at-law, identified his brother's body, and stated that he had not practised medicine since the previous October on account of epilepsy. He mentioned, too, that his brother had been in the habit of taking narcotics to relieve insomnia. Dr. Dawtrey Drewitt then stated that, when called to Myers's apartment at 8 a.m. on Tuesday, he found him "lying insensible on the bed", and despite maintaining artificial respiration by a team of six doctors he never regained consciousness. In evidence Dr. Walter Colman stated that he had known the deceased for six years but had never prescribed for him, and when called on Tuesday he found him "to be under the influence of some narcotic". It is noteworthy that Drewitt made no reference to any medication that Myers might have taken. Finally, George Walter Prothero, tutor of King's College, Cambridge, stated that he had been with the deceased on Monday afternoon and evening when he "seemed to be in unusually good spirits". The jury returned the following verdict: "The deceased died from asphyxia when in a state of coma, following an epileptic attack, and accelerated by a dose of some narcotic, while suffering from disease of the kidneys". Taylor and Marsh have rightly cast doubts on the time of Myers's death as his friends, relations, and medical attendants continued to protect him from the "odious legal and religious consequences of a verdict of suicide". They argue, too, that since Myers regularly took chloral there must have been some evidence which would distinguish an overdose of chloral from other causes of coma. They have also ascertained that at the time of death it was raining; there was a southerly wind with temperatures ranging from 40°F to 44°F, and rightly query Colman's motive in discussing the weather. "Why is Colman so apologetic . . . and why do we need to know about the weather? Maybe Colman's comments conceal the fact that Dr Myers had been dead for more than 30 hours?" Taylor and Marsh are undoubtedly correct in their assumption. The fact that Drewitt had suppressed his knowledge that Myers was under the influence of a narcotic, whereas Colman had mentioned it in evidence, does suggest that Drewitt was covering up for his dead friend. The latter probably also prolonged the alleged period of unconsciousness as the advanced decomposition of the body indicated that Myers had been dead for more than thirty hours. But clear proof of a cover-up comes from Hughlings Jackson's blunt statement in *Brain* (1898) when there was no longer any need for a medical conspiracy. "The patient died, January 1894" he wrote, "from an overdose of chloral".

But Arthur Myers's death was not the end of his contributions to neuropsychiatry and psychical research. In the same year Frank Podmore in *Apparitions and Thought Transference: An Examination of the Evidence of Telepathy* (1894) mentioned Arthur Myers's involvement in experiments in thought transference; and his long collaboration with Professor Henry Sidgwick was published as "Census of hallucinations" (1894). A year later, some of his symptoms re-emerged in his brother's paper on "The subliminal self" (1895). It will be recalled that Arthur Myers had described his epileptic experiences to Hughlings Jackson as a feeling of "double consciousness". This confirmed Frederic's notion of an unconscious subliminal secondary self possessing knowledge of the past and future. During his youth Frederick had shared Arthur's *déjà vu* experiences, which were accompanied by feelings of precognition. Frederick believed that such experiences represented the recollection of past waking experiences or of suddenly evoked dreams including memories of the spirits of the departed. Such supernormal experiences were appreciated only by the subliminal self and were not shared by the supra-liminal. But Frederic Myers went beyond a causal relation-ship, and postulated that the dreamer may, in some super-normal manner, have visited the scenes encountered, or anti-cipated the experiences he had undergone.

The brothers were linked in another of Frederick's theories. He believed that mental and emotional experiences could be transmitted by imprinting of the mother's emotions on to the foetus and that these imprints, together with others from ancestral lives, were possessed only by the subliminal self. It was mainly on the basis of his theory of the subliminal self that Frederic Myers launched an optimistic cosmic philo-sophy which came out posthumously in two volumes as *Human Personality and its Survival of Bodily Death* (1903). After mentioning in the preface that Arthur had "passed away", F. W. H. Myers then paid tribute to his brother's constant help on "all points medical". Although it cannot be ascertained whether Arthur Myers's spirit survived death, as Frederic believed, it is however, certain that his brain has become the paradigm of temporal lobe epilepsy.

Hughlings Jackson's Influence on European Psychiatry

When he joined the Medico-Psychological Association in 1866 Hughlings Jackson was a 31-year-old assistant physician at the National Hospital, but his writings show that he maintained an interest in psychiatry throughout his career. He contributed six papers to the *Journal of Mental Science*, another six to the *West Riding Asylum Medical Reports*, and more than twice this number to other journals. But at home his contributions were received in "contemptuous silence", and Spillane (1976) considers that they "were more appreciated earlier abroad". Although most psychiatrists ignored his writings, occasionally they were scathingly attacked as in an unsigned review in the *Journal of Psychological Medicine* (1876) edited by Forbes Winslow. Hughlings Jackson's "On the localisation of movements in the brain" first appeared in the *Lancet* (1873), and was reprinted as a separate pamphlet by J. and A. Churchill (1875). The anonymous reviewer criticised him for three reasons. First for applauding the animal experiments of Hitzig and Ferrier; secondly for dividing nervous diseases into 'destroying' and 'discharging' lesions, and thirdly for his lack of literary fluency. The reviewer emphasized Jackson's "obscurity of thought, crude notions, doubtful premises, disputable conclusions and his tendency

. . . of devising new words or misapplying old ones". His 'destroying' and 'discharging' lesions were ridiculed as being as "susceptible of proof as the vibrations of Hartley", while Jackson's tribute to the experimental observations of Hitzig and Ferrier was brushed aside with the comment that "these experiments are still, in the opinion of many members of our profession, *sub judice*, and are openly questioned by Burdon-Sanderson, Putnam and others".

Further, Hughlings Jackson was challenged to apply his ideas on insanity to patients in psychiatric hospitals. "I have been misunderstood to put forward the hypothesis of dissolution as a basis for classification of cases of insanity for clinical purposes", he complained in 1881 (II, 3), "and have been asked to go to some lunatic asylum and show how the cases of patients there could be classified under it". Despite the fact that Hughlings Jackson constantly proclaimed that he lacked the experience of an 'alienist' physician, and was merely suggesting an alternative system of classification, further criticism prompted him to clarify his meaning in "Remarks on the diagnosis and treatment of diseases of the brain" (1888): "I have been asked to go into an asylum", he wrote (II, 365), "and show how the cases of patients in it could be classified on that principle (dissolutions). But what I really said was the classifications (on the principle of evolution), valuable as a means of extending our knowledge, would be useless, or of little use, for direct practical purposes". Hughlings Jackson was well aware that his ideas were difficult to understand, and jokingly compared them to the "Love of God, in that it passeth all understanding". He also knew that his detractors called him "a Bedlamite theorist", a label he often used to describe himself after his more erudite lectures to medical students. This lack of understanding, and the general neglect of Hughlings Jackson's writings on psychiatry, was commented on by George Wilson (1899), Medical Superintendent of Mavisbank Asylum. "In this connection much light has been lost on the subject of mental disease by insufficient attention to the teachings of Hughlings Jackson. He pointed out long ago", wrote Wilson, "that in dissolution of nerve function, we must have regard to the two kinds of lesions and two kinds of symptoms, the primary, or negative, and the secondary or positive".

Historians should concern themselves not only with actual events but also with omissions, one of which is that Hughlings Jackson, unlike his younger contemporaries and co-editors of *Brain*, Sir David Ferrier and Sir James Crichton-Browne, was never elected to an honorary membership of the Medico-Psychological Association. Another is the lack of an obituary in the *Journal of Mental Science*, although the same journal carried a five-page one of Sir David Ferrier by T. Grainger Stewart (1928). There is, therefore, some evidence to suggest that British psychiatrists either ignored Hughlings Jackson's contributions to neuropsychiatry, or they merely 'misunderstood' them.

It can be shown, too, that this attitude persisted after his death. Nearly a decade later, one of Jackson's most brilliant disciples, Sir Henry Head (1861–1940), remarked on the general apathy among British physicians and psychiatrists, in co-operating in research on mental illnesses. "In 1901 I described certain mental changes associated with disease of the heart and lungs", wrote Head in 1918, "and showed that they formed another aspect of referred visceral pain. This work fell dead; for those who were interested in morbid conditions of the internal organs cared nothing for changes in the mental state of the patient; on the other hand the alienist denied the facts, because of the remoteness of asylum life from the conditions of hospital experience. They made no effort to discover whether such remarkable examples of the dependence of mental states on disturbances of bodily functions were really open to their investigation". Head was referring to his Goulstonian Lectures of 1901 on "Certain mental changes that accompany visceral disease"; and in 1915, gave four reasons to explain the neglect of Jackson's ideas. First, Jackson's profound modesty was such that he placed little value on his own writings, many of them being published in obscure journals. Secondly, his rather laboured literary style made them difficult to understand. In contrast to the fluency of his contemporaries, Jackson's papers contained many explanatory notes and often his most revealing ideas were half concealed in footnotes. Thirdly, his opinions, particularly those on aspects of mental disorders, were so far ahead of his time that they bore out the truth of his own dictum that "it generally takes a truth twenty five years to become known in medicine". Finally, his eulogies on the evolutionary and associationist psychology of Herbert Spencer tended to alienate psychiatrists and psychologists when Spencerian doctrines abruptly fell out of favour. There is little doubt that Jackson over-valued Spencer's influence on him at the expense of his own originality, an opinion shared by Charles Mercier (1912) and Jonathan Hutchinson (1911). Of Spencer, Mercier wrote: ". . . I always thought — and in this I think Sir Jonathan Hutchinson agrees — that Dr. Jackson gave Spencer far too much credit as the founder and suggestor of Dr. Jackson's own doctrines. In this opinion I have been confirmed by reading Spencer's 'Autobiography', which destroyed not only my respect for the man, but also, illogically perhaps, my faith in his doctrines. It seems impossible that the opinions of a man who depicts himself as the glorified quintessence of a prig can be worth anything". Finally, Head's reasons may be implemented by an academic consideration. British universities have, until comparatively recently, disregarded teaching and research in psychiatry, and hence Jackson lacked an academic stimulus, whereas several Continental universities had established professional chairs in psychiatry, or neuropsychiatry, since the nineteenth century. And undoubtedly Head was right to emphasize the traditional remoteness of psychiatric hospitals from general hospitals where Jackson studied psychiatric illness: a dichotomy that persisted until after the Second World War to the detriment of both.

Macdonald Critchley (1960) has pointed out that much of our appreciation of Hughlings Jackson's writings, particularly those on aphasia, has come about through the mediation of such Continental workers as Pick, von Monakow, Freud, and Sittig, who have reinterpreted them to us. Further, Henri Ey (1962) has referred to "the psychiatrists' indifference — if not opposition — towards the Jacksonian concept of psychic disturbances, and this is perhaps even more true in Anglo-Saxon than in other countries. For it seems almost inconceivable", he continued, "that the Jacksonian theory, despite the influence which it had on the early works of Adolf Meyer and on a few other isolated attempts, has never been thoroughly utilized in English-speaking countries". Jacksonian neurological principles, which had such a powerful stimulus on the advancement of British neurology during the past century, have been applied, modified, and extended to psychiatry by foreign psychiatrists, the foremost of whom was Sigmund Freud (1856–1939).

There is no doubt that Hughlings Jackson influenced Freud although opinions vary as to what extent. Binswanger (1936) has stated emphatically that Jacksonian neurological principles exerted a decisive effect as they coincided with Freud's exchanging neurology for psychoanalysis. And Stengel (1953) has shown that Freud quoted approvingly from two of Jackson's papers on aphasia. They both adhered to the principles of concomitance, and Angel (1961) has suggested that Freud 'borrowed' the term 'dependent concomitant' from him. Freud, like Jackson, rejected a strict localisation of speech, and in his critical study, few authorities were spared with the exception of Hughlings Jackson whom he regarded as his mentor in this sphere. This passage clearly shows that Freud adopted Jacksonian evolutionary principles: "In assessing the functions of the speech apparatus under pathological conditions", wrote Freud (1891) (translated by Stengel (1953)), "we are adopting as a guiding principle Hughlings Jackson's doctrine that all these modes of reaction represent instances of functional retrogression (disinvolution) of a highly organized apparatus, and therefore correspond to previous states of its functional development. This means that under all circumstances an arrangement of associations which, having been acquired later, belongs to a higher level of functioning, will be lost, while an earlier and simpler one will be preserved. From this point of view a great number of aphasic phenomena can be explained". This is Freud's first reference to regression, which had an important application in his psychopathology, and according to Stengel (1953) stemmed from Jackson's 'reduction' to a more primitive form of language. Support for this opinion comes from Peter Amacher (1965) and K. Levin (1978), while Roy Grinker (1939) compared psychoanalytical repression with neurological inhibition, and found that they are dynamically identical, a conclusion shared by Riese (1958).

Jackson related 'recurrent utterances' to the patient's conversation and activities immediately before the onset of aphasia; to the intensity of the emotional state when trying to speak, and to the severity of the lesion. For example, one patient suffered from aphasia after being rendered unconscious by a blow on the head, and could only reiterate: "I want protection". Another was a clerk, who had a stroke immediately after compiling a catalogue, and his 'recurrent utterance' was: "List complete". And the following passage from Freud's essay on aphasia reads like part of his chapter on errors and slips of the tongue in *Psychopathology of Everyday Life* published ten years later. "Paraphasia, i.e. mistakes in the use of words, in aphasic patients, does not differ from the incorrect use and the distortion of words which the healthy person can observe in himself in states of fatigue, or of divided attention, or under the influence of disturbing effects – the kind of thing that frequently happens to our lecturers and causes the listener painful embarrassment".

Stengel (1954) states that Freud transposed physiological concepts from his essay on aphasia into such psychodynamic terms as projection, representation, repression, and over-determination, while Riese (1958) includes Freud's explanation of pain, conversion, and hallucinatory dreams as other neurophysiological vestiges, re-emerging in psychoanalysis. Freud's many quotations from Hughlings Jackson's two papers on aphasia (1878/9), and from his Croonian lectures (1884), indicate that he had read them very carefully, and thereby acquired much more useful information on aspects of Jacksonian neurodynamics which he transformed into Freudian psychodynamics. Further, in these papers, Hughlings Jackson discussed local and general dissolutions including dreams. He mentioned unconscious processes in delirium, the 'factors' of the 'insanities', subject and object consciousness, and the principles of evolution and its reverse, dissolution, giving rise to negative and positive symptoms. Stengel (1963) believes that some of these aspects of Jackson's ideas "contributed to the foundations of psychoanalytic theory".

In particular, Hughlings Jackson stressed the regressive nature of all mental disorders, and described dreams as "physiological insanity", two aspects of his writings which were subsequently fully exploited by Freud. Stengel (1954) also suggests that Freud's structure of the personality had much in common with the three Jacksonian functional levels. The close similarity between Jackson's negative and positive symptoms, and Bleulerian psychodynamics, has been commented on by Riese (1954): ". . . The neurologist familiar with the doctrine of Jackson, has no difficulty in identifying the Bleulerian psychodynamics with Jacksonian neuro-dynamics, or over-activity of the spared parts, the so-called release phenomena. Still more surprising in this respect is Bleuler's interpretation of secondary symptoms as results, or more or less successful adjustments, of the primary defect . . . . Thus, the identity of Jacksonian and Bleulerian views seems almost complete. But it remains purely incidental since Bleuler never mentioned Jackson; nor did the name appear in his bibliography comprising 850 other references." But Stengel

(1963) believes that Freud was the link between them, and argues that Bleuler's psychopathology of schizophrenia was based mainly on Freudian ideas, particularly on his observations on abnormal thought contents, which illuminate the nature of delusions. Other similarities are Jackson's positive symptoms, Bleuler's primary symptoms, and their comparison of dreams with the psychoses. Stengel (1963) concludes that Bleuler's "hierarchy of schizophrenic symptoms, so similar to Jackson's differentiation of the symptoms of nervous disorders, was inspired by Freud's interest in the positive symptoms of mental disorders from which the postulation of primary symptoms followed by logical necessity. Freud, then, was the intermediary between Jackson and Bleuler".

Although Freud did not agree with Jackson's statement that states of consciousness are synonymous with states of mind, there is, nevertheless, general support for the view that some Jacksonian ideas may be traced in psychoanalytical theory. Angel (1961) considers that whereas Jackson "sought physical explanations for disordered states of the nervous system; Freud sought psychological explanations for disordered states of mind", and concludes that "it is well known that Freud's earlier views on the relations between mind and the nervous system were greatly influenced by Jackson . . .".

In his psychoanalytical writings Freud referred to Jackson only in a footnote in *The Interpretation of Dreams* (1900) on the connection between insanity and dreams. Freud's lack of acknowledgement stemmed, in Stengel's opinion, from the clean break he made with his neurological past once he began to develop psychoanalysis. Gregory Zilboorg (1959), on the other hand, has commented on Freud's capacity "for forgetting the sources of his information", while Jean Delay (1953) was more emphatic, and considers that Freud so "thoroughly neglected to cite his sources as to astonish even his faithful disciple Jones". Delay believes that Freud could also have become acquainted indirectly with Hughlings Jackson's writings through the mediation of Théodule Ribot

(1839–1916), who reapplied Jacksonian principles in his psychopathology. In Freud's day, Ribot was well known, and his books were prominently displayed in all the bookshops when Freud lived in Paris between 1885 and 1886.

Finally, Freud and Jackson shared a common interest in the technique of free association. Freud subscribed to *Brain*, where Hughlings Jackson's papers on aphasia had appeared in the January and October issues of 1879: in the July issue Francis Galton (1822–1911) described in "Psychometric experiments" a word association test, and, in this passage, discussed unconscious processes: "Perhaps the strongest of the impressions left by these experiments regards the multifariousness of the work done by the mind in a state of half-unconsciousness, and the valid reason they afford for believing in the existence of still deeper strata of mental operations, sunk wholly below the level of consciousness, which may account for such mental phenomena as cannot otherwise be explained." Galton's biographer, D. W. Forrest (1974), has assumed that Freud had read Galton's paper, and suggests that it may have stimulated his adoption of the free association technique in the 1890s. But Freud's recent biographer R. W. Clark (1980) has drawn attention to another possible origin of this technique in Ludwig Börne's essay on "The art of becoming an original writer in three days", which Freud read as a youth. On re-reading it he admitted that "it could well have been the real source of my originality". At all events there is no doubt that Galton's paper deeply impressed Hughlings Jackson, then joint editor of *Brain*, since Sir Farquhar Buzzard (1934), who became his house physician in 1899, states that he often advised students to practise this technique. Buzzard recalled that Hughlings Jackson often asked them to think over the topic that had most aroused their interest, and with a notebook at hand, allow "the mind to wander at random around it, and jotting down the speculations it may cause". Undoubtedly this was Hughlings Jackson's own method of considering the implications of his clinical findings from which he endeavoured to forge general neurological principles for, as McEachern (1935) succinctly puts it, he was essentially "a compounder of ideas and precepts".

From the Vienna of Freud, Hughlings Jackson's ideas, a few decades later, were re-echoed in Warsaw through the neo-Jacksonian writings of Jan Mazurkiewicz (1871–1947), appointed in 1919 as the first professor of psychiatry at Warsaw University. First in "Les intégrations nerveuses" (1935), and in greater detail in the two volumes of his monumental *Wstęp do Psychofizjologii Normalnej* (1950), Mazurkiewicz combined Pavlovian psychophysiology with neurophysiology of the vegetative system, chronogenetic localization, and Jacksonian neurodynamics, the last mentioned being our only concern. Mazurkiewicz transposed Jacksonian neurodynamics of the highest centres into a psychical hierarchy progressing from the most automatic, simple, and well organised, to the voluntary, complex, and least organised. He then combined Jacksonian neurodynamics with evolution of the emotions. During evolution spontaneous instinctive impulses shed their impetuous nature, and their lack of restraint, as they become integrated into the intellectually based higher emotions of adults. Similarly perceptual functions undergo evolution and its reverse in dissolution.

In his second volume, "Dyssolucja aktywności korowo-psychicznej", and particularly in the chapter on "Jacksonowska teoria dyssolucji. Dążności neojacksonistyczne", Mazurkiewicz discussed Jacksonian dissolutions, which he divided into rapid, slow (as in schizophrenia), prelogical, and those of lucid perception. Infections, toxins, and trauma may also cause dissolutions. He followed Hughlings Jackson in recognising that dissolutions cause negative and positive symptoms. Mazurkiewicz believed that a dissolution disturbed normal, logical, and causally related mental activities, leading to the appearance of prelogical functions and their primitive impulses.

Mazurkiewicz, however, did not regard manic-depressive psychosis as a dissolution, on account of its genetic loading, which, together with the dementias (caused by destruction of the anatomical substrata of memory), he excluded from his consideration of the effects of reversals of evolution. He regarded the psychoneuroses as manifestations of the first stage of an emotional and perceptual dissolution, and considered personality disorders, and subnormality, as manifestations of the abnormal development of psychical function.

The evolution of lucidity was one of Mazurkiewicz's most important concepts. The consciousness of a baby, for example, differs from that of an adult, and each stage in its progression to adult life involves increasing lucidity. In the development of complete lucidity, prelogical consciousness is transformed into logical and causally related consciousness. Dissolution reverses this progression as in oneiroid states, schizophrenia, or other states of altered perception, such as the depersonalisation-derealisation syndrome, with its loss of control of the highest psychical centres, and the intrusion of strange and alien mental phenomena. Thus through his concept of the dissolution of lucidity of consciousness, Mazurkiewicz enlarged the range of clinical disturbances of the highest level of psychical life. In so doing he formulated his own classification of the schizophrenias. He strictly limited the diagnosis of schizophrenia to a specific genetic and constitutional illness with a characteristic age of onset, typical symptomatology, and running a definite course; and he used 'schizophreniform' only in reference to the schizophrenic process. Other psychiatric disorders, characterised by illusions, hallucinations, and delusions, he classified as "acute or chronic prelogical psychoses". Mazurkiewicz's neo-Jacksonian ideas have been overlooked, although Kaczyński (1975) has rightly claimed that he "placed Polish scientific psychiatry in the forefront of the international field".

Jackson's writings were particularly well received in the neighbouring central European capital of Prague. In dedicating

Die agrammatischen Sprachstörungen (1913) to him, Arnold Pick (1891–1924) described Jackson as "the deepest thinker in neuropathology of the past century"; and Otto Sittig translated his study of convulsions as *J. Hughlings Jackson's Eine Studie über Krämpfe* (1926). Professor Ladislaus Benedek (1935) of Debrecen in Hungary has briefly surveyed Jackson's life and writings, as also has Georg Schaltenbrand (1936) of Würzburg. Hughlings Jackson's writings were introduced to Italy by Leonardo Bianchi, in *Trattato di psichiatria* (1905), where melancholia is discussed in Jacksonian terms as an overaction of inferior centres. Bianchi also explained psychopathological states as a dissolution of the most recently acquired elements causing impulsive and disruptive behaviour. But the most comprehensive biographical account together with a detailed bibliography of his writings has been presented by José María López Piñero of Valencia in *John Hughlings Jackson (1835–1911). Evolucionismo y Neurología* (1973). From Russia, Marie de Manacéïne (1897) commented on Jackson's observation that retinal blood vessels are contracted during sleep; and that purposive movements may be made in a deep coma. After remarking on the long neglect of Jackson's ideas, Luria (1966) discussed approvingly his contributions to speech disorders. In his discussion of psychical phenomena associated with epilepsy Muskens (1928) of Amsterdam accepts Hughlings Jackson's explanation of automatisms as manifestations of loss of control of the higher centres. He does not, however, consider that this explanation helps in understanding the problem, and raises the question as to whether psychosis "always occurs in association with an epileptic fit."

Hughlings Jackson had an extensive knowledge of French medical literature, doubtlessly stimulated by his early association with Brown-Séquard, and his ideas exerted their greatest influence in France. Among the numerous authorities quoted by Jackson are Claude Bernard, G. B. Duchenne, M. J. P. Flourens, A. Trousseau, E. F. A. Vulpian, A. Pitres, and

J. Falret. Jackson always credited Bravais with the first description of 'epileptiform seizures', and as early as 1868, he debated with Paul Broca on speech disorders at the Norwich Congress of the British Association for the Advancement of Science. Most frequently Jackson quoted from the writings of Professor J.-M. Charcot, who first called unilateral fits 'épilepsie bravais-jacksonnienne': they met in 1886 at the B.M.A. annual meeting in Brighton, where Victor Horsley gave a pioneering account of brain surgery and demonstrated some patients. Charcot began the discussion by graciously congratulating "the surgeon and physician who had so accurately diagnosed these cases"; and Jackson then stressed the diagnostic significance of focal fits as indicators of a "very local change" in the brain.

While Charcot may be credited with introducing the eponym 'Jacksonian', Hughlings Jackson, in return, revived 'Baillarger's principle', first mentioned during a discussion at the Medical Academy of France. Baillarger noticed that some aphasic patients lose the motor component of speech, and despite every effort are unable to repeat certain words. This is associated with the spontaneous utterance of the same words when in an emotional state. For example, Alajouanine (1960) had a patient, who was unable to give the Christian name of her daughter on request. When she became upset about her forgetfulness she exclaimed: "My poor Jacqueline, now I don't know your name any longer". Alajouanine states that this observation would have been overlooked in France had not Hughlings Jackson constantly stressed its significance, and hence he suggests the joint eponym of 'the principle of Baillarger–Jackson'.

But it was mainly through the now forgotten works of Théodule Ribot (1839–1916), teacher and predecessor of Pierre Janet (1859–1947), that Hughlings Jackson's writings became well known in France, and subsequently exerted a strong influence on French psychiatry. In *La psychologie anglaise contemporaine* (1870), Ribot discussed the writings

of such associationist and evolutionary psychologists as
Spencer, Lewes, Bain, and Mill, and when formulating his
psychopathology, Ribot naturally turned for clinical guidance
(as he was not a physician) to Hughlings Jackson, the foremost exponent of Spencerian evolutionary psychology. He
then reapplied Jacksonian neurological principles in his psychopathology of disorders of memory, will, and personality.

In *Les maladies de la mémoire* (1881) Ribot discussed the
failure of memory with loss of the most recent memories and
retention of the oldest ones; obliteration of the most complex
memories with retention of the simplest ones; erasure of the
most voluntary memories while more automatic ones remain,
and loss of the least organized memories with retention of
the most original ones. This sequential deterioration of
memory became known in France as "Ribot's Law", although
he always acknowledged that it was based on the application
of a Jacksonian principle. Ribot also distinguished between
general and local dissolutions of motor or sensory pathways,
but preferred to call them partial rather than local. By strictly
applying Jacksonian principles to partial amnesia, Ribot distinguished between sensory amnesia, or agnosia, and motor
amnesia, or apraxia. In *Les maladies de la volonté* (1883)
Ribot discussed the obliteration of voluntary activities as a
negative symptom accompanied by increased automatic ones.
Mania and drunkenness are two common volitional disturbances and, on the same basis, Ribot also attempted to explain
irresistible impulses to commit suicide, kleptomania, and
erotomania. When highest level awareness is affected, automatisms may emerge as positive symptoms and, like Jackson,
Ribot compared them to epileptic dreams with somnambulism.

Jackson was impressed by Ribot's application of his neurological principles in his psychopathology, and in his Croonian
lectures (1884) referred "with great respect to the most
valuable and highly original work which Ross, Ribot and
Mercier have done". He described *Les maladies de la personnalité* (1885) as "a very valuable book", and was particularly

interested in Ribot's theory of hallucinations. A dissolution of the personality first brings about an alienation of consciousness which appears to assume an independent existence. Ribot compared this detachment of consciousness with other dissolutions of the personality unaccompanied by an alienation of consciousness. Jean Delay (1953) regards this distinction as a remarkable anticipation of the difference between hallucinations and hallucinosis: the latter being a local phenomenon caused by sensory irritation and therefore a perceptual disturbance, whereas hallucinations are disorders of judgement or belief.

Pierre Janet described Ribot's psychopathology as the "breviary of psychologists and physicians", and applied his ideas in the explanation of psychasthenia — a term he preferred to neurasthenia. Janet subdivided states of reality into five levels, which have some similarities with Jacksonian functional levels, the highest signifying the maximum capacity for the appreciation of reality. At a superficial level Janet included such psychasthenic crises as acute anxiety states whereas other disturbances of reality begin at lower levels. These similarities puzzled Rouart (1950), as Janet had never read Jackson's works, but he overlooked an indirect inheritance through the works of Ribot as mentioned by Delay (1953) and Ellenberger (1970).

Among other neo-Jacksonian writings are those by C. von Monakow and R. Mourgue in their *Introduction biologique à l'étude de la neurologie et de la psychopathologie, intégration et désintégration de la fonction* (1928) described by Delay (1953) as a "veritable manifesto of neo-Jacksonianism". Von Monakow and Mourgue combined Jacksonian neurodynamics with the *élan vital* of Bergson, and they postulated that an instinctive and formative principle called 'horme' is the driving force of the organism's genesis, growth, and welfare.

It was mainly through the writings of Henri Ey (1900–77) that the originality of Hughlings Jackson's neurological principles re-emerged from the laudatory acclaim that first

greeted the works of Ribot and Janet. Ey emerged and modified Jacksonian neurodynamics with aspects of Freudian
psychoanalysis and Janet's phenomenology, with emphasis
on the reflective explanation of the contents of consciousness,
in the formulation of his concept of organo-dynamic psychiatry. Ey considers that all mental disorders involve a defect
of consciousness, but in this respect, he widened Jackson's
ideas of consciousness. In Ey's opinion the field of consciousness is the dynamic organisation of actuality — being the consciousness of *something* in a wider sense than the identification
of external objects. The other aspect of consciousness involves
the ego, or personality, implying consciousness of being
somebody. In normal health, consciousness and the unconscious are in a dynamic equilibrium. Though Ey agreed with
the Freudian notion of regression, originating from Jackson's
'disinvolution', he was totally opposed to Freud's undue
emphasis on unconscious forces at the expense of consciousness and reality. Weakness in the organisation of consciousness
has more relevance, he believed, in psychiatric disorders than
unconscious mechanisms. And as waking life is obviously at a
higher level than sleep, it formed the foundation of Ey's
structure of the psychic being.

Mental disorders, in Ey's opinion, have regressive, symbolic,
and imaginary aspects, corresponding to Hughlings Jackson's
negative disturbance. And a dissolution leaves an organo-
clinical discrepancy between negative and positive symptoms
which is filled by the reaction of the personality. In his modification and reapplication of Jacksonian principles to psychic
life in local and general dissolutions Philip Evans (1972) has
shown that Ey took a *via media* between neurology and
psychiatry without subordinating one discipline to the other.
In formulating organo-dynamic psychiatry Henri Ey laid
down these basic tenets:

(1) *Psychological*
Mental disorders are implied in the organisation of the person

and involve 'destructuration', regression, dissolution or the 'reduction' of psychical life to an inferior or archaic level. Ey emphasized that mental illness is implicit in every individual, and is analogous to dreaming when the organisation of the psychic being is temporarily 'destructured'.

(2) Phenomenological

The structure of mental illness, being basically negative, involves a deficit as in dementia and schizophrenia, but less obviously in paranoia occurring at a higher level of mental pathology. Nevertheless defects may be revealed by a phenomenological analysis of the temporo-spatial structure of consciousness. Negative symptoms are even less apparent in the neuroses and personality disorders, and may emerge as immaturity or instability. Thus Ey regards mental illness as a disorder of reality reflecting the fantastic or imaginary aspects of experience.

(3) Clinical

All mental disorders, on account of their evolutionary dynamic structure correspond, in Ey's opinion, to dissolutions of the psychical organisation along two dimensions. First in the field of consciousness there are such acute psychoses as manic-depressive psychosis, transient delirium, and oneiroid states. Secondly, disorganisation of different levels of the personality structure causes such chronic conditions as the dementias and schizophrenia at the lowest level, paraphrenia at a higher level, and states of disequilibrium such as the neuroses and character disorders at the highest level. Negative symptoms may be revealed by a comparative analysis, whereas positive symptoms may be elicited by phenomenological analysis. The sleep–dream pattern is valid in all aspects of psychopathology, since the phenenology of dreams and oneiroid thinking are forms of fantasy life. Henri Ey was opposed to regarding mental disorders as disease entities, and preferred to discuss them as syndromes or pathological reactions, having numerous predisposing factors.

In Ey's (1962) opinion mental illness represents both a shrinking of existence, and a pathology of freedom. He agreed with Hughlings Jackson that "disease does not create, it sets free". Finally, Ey considers that Hughlings Jackson's contribution to organo-dynamic psychiatry, far from being an outmoded application of Spencerian evolutionary philosophy, is "in accordance with the most profound trends in contemporary medical thinking".

North American and British Jacksonians

Hughlings Jackson's writings were acclaimed in America, where he had many friends. The best known was Silas Weir Mitchell (1829–1914), who dedicated to him his "Lectures on diseases of the nervous system, especially in women" (1881), "with warm personal regards, and in grateful acknowledgement of his services to the science of medicine". After the Civil War, Weir Mitchell's practice included increasing numbers of psychiatric patients, most of whom were diagnosed as hysteria or neurasthenia, the last-mentioned diagnosis having been introduced in 1869 by George M. Beard (1837–83), lecturer in nervous diseases at New York University. Hughlings Jackson often quoted from Weir Mitchell's "magnificent work" on phantom limb phenomena. As one of the editors of *Brain*, Jackson arranged for the publication in the first volume of Weir Mitchell's "Some of the lessons of neurotomy" (1878), and a review of A. M. Hamilton's *Nervous Diseases, their Description and Treatment* (1878). But credit for the first American textbook of neurology belongs to W. A. Hammond (1828–1900). In *A Treatise on Diseases of the Nervous System* (1871) Hammond discussed Jackson's views on aphasia and, in the 1881 edition, referred approvingly to his writings on epilepsy. On a visit to London in 1898, Weir Mitchell called on Hughlings Jackson, who arranged a meeting with Herbert Spencer.

One of the earliest Americans to study under Hughlings Jackson was Francis Turquand Mills (1827–1903), who became Professor of Nervous Diseases at Washington University. In 1874 Roberts Bartholow (1831–1904) electrically stimulated the human brain, provoking muscular contractions of the contralateral extremity, and thereby confirmed the clinical observations of Hughlings Jackson, and the animal experiments of Fritsch, Hitzig, and Ferrier. From Edward Seguin (1843–98), Professor of Diseases of the Nervous System at the College of Physicians and Surgeons, New York, Jackson 'borrowed' (with consistent acknowledgement) the term 'signal' symptom signifying the site of onset of focal epilepsy.

In 1870 James Jackson Putnam (1846–1918) accompanied Hughlings Jackson on his ward rounds at the National Hospital, and ten years later, attended his lectures at the London Hospital, of which he has left the best account . . . . "It was Dr Jackson's custom to draw a pyramid upon the blackboard", wrote Putnam (1913), "which should stand for the hierarchy of the cerebral functions, the more fundamental of them being represented by the basal portions of the pyramid, the more complex and recently acquired, by the apex portion. His idea then was that when the hierarchy of functions represented by this pyramid suffers derangement *at any part* . . . the attempt at a re-establishment of some sort of equilibrium is always such that the new arrangement tends to safeguard itself by accentuating the more fundamental of its powers, while sacrificing, so far as necessary, the more elaborate. . . . In general 'devolution', to use Jackson's term, follows, or reverses the lines of evolution, and seeks, first, to [sic] the more vital interests of the individual; and still more so, of the race." In 1893 Putnam became the first Professor of Disease of the Nervous System at Harvard, and on Hughlings Jackson's death, recalled his "kindly, thoughtful face, full of refinement, charm, and with lines that lent themselves readily both to the expression of humor and to quiet utterances of firm decision". And in his *Human Motives* (1915), Putnam referred to

Jackson as "one of the great philosophers of medicine". Another American who applied Jacksonian principles during his sixty years of practice was Charles K. Mills (1843-1931), Professor of Neurology at the University of Pennsylvania. In his address to the Philadelphia Neurological Society on "The evolution of our knowledge of the brain during the last sixty years" (1927), Mills stressed the usefulness of Jacksonian functional levels together with his definition of brain centres as sites where movements and impressions are represented with greater measure than elsewhere. He had studied the effects of brain tumours with relation to Jacksonian levels as he did "not know anyone better for a neurologist to follow"; and during the discussion exclaimed: "The difficulty is that we do not all have the brain of a Jackson, a Laycock, a Bain, or a Ferrier. I am certain that I do not have it; yet I understand this theory of highest triple representation". This was more than could be claimed by most of Jackson's British colleagues, who failed to take the trouble to understand him. Among other American admirers of Hughlings Jackson's was Charles Loomis Dana (1852-1935) who was the first American to give the Hughlings Jackson Memorial Lecture in 1927 at the Royal Society of Medicine. Bernard Sachs (1858-1944) spent part of his postgraduate studies with Hughlings Jackson at Queen Square. On his return to New York, Sachs was appointed to the staff of the Mount Sinai Hospital, where in 1887 he described amaurotic familial idiocy. His nephew Ernest Sachs (1879-1938) carried on the Jacksonian tradition in 1907 through his uncle's arranging for him to work with Sir Victor Horsley. Sachs was warmly received in London, and although retired, Hughlings Jackson still took a keen interest in all Horsley's work, particularly his physiological experiments, and it is likely that Sachs met him, and certain that he inherited Jackson's teachings through his close links with Horsley (Sachs 1957). Finally Jelliffe and White (1915) in their *Diseases of the Nervous System. A Textbook of Neurology and Psychiatry* refer approvingly to the Jacksonian functional hierarchy of brain levels.

Recently American contributions have concentrated on re-assessing Jackson's contributions within a historical context, the foremost exponent being Oswei Temkin in his classic *The Falling Sickness* (1945) and (1971), wherein he not only presents an exhaustive historical survey of Jackson's contributions to epilepsy but also his ideas on mental disorders. Anglo-American endeavour is represented by Clarke and O'Malley's *The Human Brain and Spinal Cord* (1968) offering a biographical outline together with extracts from Jackson's most significant writings. *Garrison's History of Neurology* (1969), revised by Lawrence C. McHenry and William G. Lennox; and *The Founders of Neurology* (1957), edited by Webb Haymaker and Francis Schiller, provide a panoramic view of Jackson's contributions and emphasize his biographical details. Of particular psychiatric interest is a short study by Menninger, Ellenberger, Pruyser, and Mayman (1958) on Hughlings Jackson's contribution to the unitary concept of mental illness. In particular they stress Hughlings Jackson's influence on Henri Ey in that they were both reluctant psychiatric nosologists and preferred to regard clinical syndromes as degrees of 'dissolution'. Nielsen and Thompson (1947) discuss Jackson's pioneering contributions to disturbances of recognition and syndromes of familiarity and strangeness. In their comprehensive *Epilepsy and Related Disorders* (1960) Lennox and Lennox give a biographical outline of Hughlings Jackson together with his main contributions to neurology; and in *Mind, Brain and Adaptation in the 19th Century* (1970) Robert M. Young has provided a useful background to his application of Spencerian evolutionary principles and those of other associationists. In two original papers Greenblatt (1965) and (1970) has illuminated Jackson's pioneering work on aphasia in relation to that of Broca, and traced the early influences determining the direction of his neurological observations. The background to

Hughlings Jackson's ideas on mind–body relations has been fully surveyed by Engelhardt (1972) (1975); and in *The Unique Legacy of Dr Hughlings Jackson* (1970), Arthur M. Lassek, Sr. has not only provided the first brief biography, but also brought his writings into contemporary focus. In *Textbook of Neurology* (1927) Dr I. S. Weschler, Professor of Clinical Neurology at Columbia, stated that Hughlings Jackson's writings were beginning to "illuminate psychiatry", which was probably a reference to the writings of Dr. Adolf Meyer (1866–1950). After qualifying in Zurich, Meyer attended Hughlings Jackson's ward rounds and lectures in 1891. When he moved to America, Menninger *et al.* stated that Meyer introduced the Kraepelinian classification of mental disorders, which he subsequently regretted as he evolved a unitary concept of mental illness. Meyer's biographer, Lief (1948) states that this change of direction occurred when he came across a critical article by Morton Prince entitled "Hughlings Jackson and the connection between mind and brain" (1891). This stirred his memories of Queen Square, and, after re-reading Hughlings Jackson, Meyer began to apply his principles in psychiatry. After he became Professor of Psychiatry at Johns Hopkins, Meyer attempted to unify anatomy, physiology, and psychology, together with the patients' life style, into a comprehensive biological system. He studied the interaction with the environment of the patient's whole personality in terms of a non-dogmatic psychobiological theory, and considered patients' reaction types as patterns of misdirected energy. But whereas Jackson had strictly separated physical phenomena from mental ones in order to clarify neurology, Meyer brought them together in his study of the whole person in relation to his environment. And he acknowledged his indebtedness to Jackson, particularly for his adoption of a hierarchical functional dynamic theory, rather than the narrower concept of structure, by referring to him as "the functional pathologist *par excellence*".

Another European-trained American who illuminated many aspects of Jackson's writings is Walter Riese (1944, 1945, 1947, 1955, 1956, 1958, 1965) of Richmond, Virginia. Many of his contributions have been mentioned but, in particular, Riese emphasized that Jackson's theory of psychiatric illnesses was based on "his masterly descriptions of post-epileptic states of mental alienation". In a long series of contributions, Max Levin (1933, 1933, 1934, 1934/5, 1936, 1936, 1937, 1938, 1938, 1939, 1939, 1945, 1953, 1960, 1962/3, 1965) of Harrisburg, Pennsylvania concentrated on reapplying Jacksonian principles in psychiatry, which had, hitherto, been neglected. ". . . Jackson inductively worked out certain general principles of mental functioning which are profoundly illuminating", wrote Levin (1933), "principles, be it shamefully admitted, which the world of psychiatry has ignored and virtually forgotten". Levin (1933) explains eidetic imagery in Jacksonian terms. Children can perceive an object, long after gazing at it, because of their intense thought associations. But loss of eidetic imagery in adults is, he believes, the consequence of brain maturation when highest centres act independently of lower ones and imagery is replaced by imagination.

He then applied the Jacksonian model of post-ictal psychosis in an attempt to formulate a pathogenesis of schizophrenia. All mental illnesses, he argues, cause a loss of such special functions of the highest centres as complex or symbolic thought, judgement, and emotion. This is accompanied by a diminution of cerebral versatility with fewer and less complex concepts, and a reduced capacity to differentiate between them. Another measure of evolution of the nervous centres is their ability to function independently, which is lost in schizophrenia and results, Levin (1936, 1938) believes, in the patient hearing 'imaginary voices' or believing that his thoughts are audible to others. Jackson, it will be recalled, held that faint images are thoughts, or an unspoken sequence of words, but in schizophrenia the ability of the highest centres to function independently is reduced and accompanied by an increased innervation of lower ones so that 'faint' images are replaced by vivid ones. Words that would, in a healthy state, be thoughts, now become audible as hallucinatory 'voices'. Levin (1934) also applied Jacksonian principles to a patient with catatonic schizophrenia when in partial remission. She was reticent when interviewed by her doctor, whereas on less formal occasions she spoke with spontaneous ease. Levin explains these differences in terms of the least automatic functions being the soonest disturbed, while the most automatic ones are less readily affected, which is analogous to Jackson's interpretation of the propositional, volitional, and emotional aspects of speech.

In the forefront of extending the Jacksonian tradition is the Montreal Neurological Institute, Canada where Hughlings Jackson memorial lectures were begun in 1935. Among the distinguished lecturers, who discussed aspects of neuropsychiatry, are Lashley (1937), Hebb (1959), Jasper (1959), Symonds (1960), Penfield (1963), Brain (1963), and Milner (1979). Research at the Institute, too, has confirmed and extended Hughlings Jackson's clinical observations. Penfield and Rasmussen (1950) have demonstrated that hallucinatory activity is confined to temporal lobe stimulation; and Jackson's observations on 'uncinate' epilepsy with automatisms have been confirmed by Feindel and Penfield (1954). In "The role of the temporal cortex in certain psychical phenomena", Penfield (1955) (cf. (1963)) has discussed various psychological, interpretative, and perceptual functions of the temporal lobe; and Feindel (1961) has shown that behavioural manifestations are more likely to be provoked by stimulation of the periamygdaloid region. In his magisterial *The Discovery of the Unconscious* (1970) Henri F. Ellenberger, Professor of Criminology at the Université de Montréal, has drawn attention to the dynamic dimension in Jackson's neurology, first applied in his studies on aphasia and epilepsy, and used in the sense of a functional process, rather than a static anatomical structure. Concerning Hughlings Jackson's general influence on psychiatry, Ellenberger considers that it 'probably' extended to Freud.

Other North Americans who have discussed aspects of Jackson's writings are Parker (1929), Langworthy (1932), Foster Kennedy (1935), McEachern (1935), Podolsky (1947) and Viets (1931, 1938, 1948), but at the risk of omitting others (such as Sir William Osler who unsuccessfully tried to persuade him to write a book), it is claimed that sufficient evidence has been presented to show that in North America, Hughlings Jackson's writings have been the subject of considerable historical scholarship, while his neurological principles have been confirmed and extended in a long series of clinical and experimental observations.

How were they received at home? Sir George Savage (1842–1921), an old friend, attempted to get them off to a good start in "Hughlings Jackson on mental disorders" (1917). Savage had attended Jackson's ward rounds at the London Hospital, and the latter reciprocated at Bethlem, where Savage attracted a large postgraduate audience. He began his lecture by admitting that British psychiatrists had, hitherto, ignored Jackson's ideas on psychiatry, and he, therefore, regarded it as "almost a duty" to make up for this neglect. After mentioning Jackson's adoption of the doctrine of concomitance, and his opinion that all mental activities are the subjective accompaniments of sensori-motor processes, Savage agreed with him that the frontal lobes are the repositories of mental functions. When discussing Jackson's 'factors' of the insanities, Savage rightly stated that he included "a good many states of mind that are not generally considered to be mental illnesses", such as dreams. "I believe it was Hughlings Jackson who said that insanity was dreaming awake", continued Savage, "while dreaming was insanity asleep". He then delineated Jackson's degrees of post-ictal insanities, and compared them to various levels of sleep, and to different degrees of drunkenness. Savage described Jackson's interpretation of imperative ideas as "something distinctly original", but confessed he had difficulty in understanding his writings, which were not "associated with fluency of expression". This was one reason, Savage claimed, for their neglect by British psychiatrists, although it does not explain their ready acceptance in France, Poland, the United States and elsewhere. In fact, Savage omitted such significant Jacksonian ideas as those on consciousness, the duality of subject and object consciousness, the organisation of symbol images, and his explanation of delusions and hallucinations which formed the core of his neuropsychiatry. But Savage's conservatism is reflected in the fourth edition of his *Insanity and Allied Neuroses* (1907) in which he still recognised 'masturbatory insanity' as a diagnostic entity.

When James Taylor (with the advice and assistance of Gordon Holmes and F. M. R. Walshe) edited the *Selected Writings of John Hughlings Jackson* (1931/2), his ideas reached a wide and appreciative audience, as the two volumes were soon out of print. In a favourable review F. L. Golla (1932) prophetically remarked on their potential usefulness in psychiatry. "Valuable as are the lessons the neurologist may still gather from Jackson's writings", he wrote, "it is the psychiatrist who, at the present epoch, is most likely to benefit from their teaching. Psychiatry has yet to find for itself a scientific basis, and there is no greater stimulus to clear thinking than the utterances of Jackson. His fundamental conception of the real significance of symptoms as the evidence of release of control is never lost sight of, and provides the clue to much that has been hopelessly entangled by the irrational attribution of positive symptoms to nervous matter that has undergone destruction". Stengel (1954) has confirmed that, even later, Jacksonian ideas "remained practically unknown among psychiatrists" until Golla's prophesies were fulfilled in the writings of Freud, Ey, Mazurkiewicz, and Meyer.

Why were Hughlings Jackson's ideas ignored by British psychiatrists? He practised during the high noon of the

Victorian asylum system when these medically administered institutions slumbered on, undisturbed in their siestas by the criticisms of a lack of progress in alleviating mental illness. There was, however, one particularly noteworthy exception. When James Crichton-Browne became medical superintendent of Wakefield Psychiatric Hospital he transformed this provincial asylum into one of the foremost neuropsychiatric research centres in Britain. And when refuting criticisms that asylum medical officers busied themselves in administration rather than research, he inadvertently revealed the true state of affairs, not in his own hospital, but in the majority of institutions. "Medical officers of these establishments are so absorbed in general and fiscal management, in farming, or in devising ill-judged amusements for their charges", wrote Crichton-Browne in 1871, "that they have no time nor energy left to devote to professional research. And it has been further asserted that when these medical officers have by any chance ventured to enter the field of original investigation, they have, as a rule, signally failed in achieving any useful results . . .". Medical superintendents of Victorian asylums formed a medical squirearchy: they lived in handsome residences; they were well provided with servants; they managed the hospital farms; and their power over this self-contained community was absolute. Despite Crichton-Browne's exhortations to undertake research, the majority of asylum medical officers tended to move from one institution to another until they, too, rose in the hierarchy. "It is upon Asylum medical officers that the obligation to watch and interrogate nervous diseases most heavily falls", exhorted Crichton-Browne in 1875, "and their opportunities of doing so are peculiarly great and excellent. Our lunatic hospitals are stored with only too vast an accumulation of pathological material, while their organization affords unusual facilities for observation and research . . .." But he pleaded in vain, as with some notable exceptions including Sir John Bucknill, Hack Tuke, Bevan Lewis, and himself, few other Victorian psychiatrists achieved any lasting eminence.

A subsidiary reason for ignoring Jacksonian principles may have been the holistic conceptual framework within which they were presented, as British psychiatrists, having been nurtured in the empirical tradition, may have regarded his unitary conception of mental disorders with more reserve than their Continental colleagues.

It should be emphasized, however, that it is not intended to imply that Jacksonian principles were ignored in Britain. On the contrary, Hughlings Jackson inspired significant contributions from leading neurologists including Sir Henry Head (1901, 1915, 1918, 1920); Kinnier Wilson (1928, 1935, 1940); Lord Brain (1935, 1951, 1958, 1958, 1959); Sir Francis Walshe (1935, 1943, 1953, 1956, 1958, 1960, 1961); Sir Charles Symonds (1959, 1960, 1966); Macdonald Critchley (1960, 1960, 1960, 1970); Purdon Martin (1945, 1949, 1973, 1975); and Denis Williams (1956, 1958, 1963), who have reinterpreted and re-applied them. Neurologists, rather than psychiatrists, have re-introduced Jacksonian neuropsychiatry to Britain and Lord Brain (1958) has drawn particular attention to two of his most significant and lasting contributions to psychiatry. First is Jackson's unitary concept of mental illness as a dissolution of the highest centres manifested as a defect of consciousness. Secondly, Brain considers that Jackson's phenomenological and causal theory of perception is still valid. It will be recalled that Jackson believed that images seen in dreams, illusions, hallucinations, and normal perception all have an equal validity as experiences. He explained "seeing faces in the fire" as the consequence of a temporary relaxation of object consciousness with increased subject consciousness. ". . . We do not see the cracks and marks in the burning coals. The cracks and marks do not produce the images of cracks and marks in us", wrote Jackson (II, 25), "they *produce faces in us*". In "On post-epileptic states" (1888/9) Hughlings Jackson emphasized the same theme when discussing mental illness. "What we call the insane man's extravagant conduct displays his will;" he wrote (I, 383), "what we call his illusions are his perceptions (memory); what we call his delusions are his beliefs (his reasoning); and what we call his caprice is evidence of his emotional change". Lord Brain (1958) concluded that Hughlings Jackson "was ahead not only of his own time, but in some respects of our own", while Sir Francis Walshe (1960) proclaimed "that we do not yet know all that we owe to him".

Sir Charles Symonds (1945, 1960) discussed recovery from concussion, beginning in the lowest and progressing through higher centres, in Jacksonian functional terms. In another paper on "Disease of mind and disorders of brain" Symonds (1960) regards manic-depressive psychosis and schizophrenia as manifestations of organic brain lesions responding, to some extent, to electroplexy, anti-depressants, or anti-psychotic medication, all acting neurologically, although he concedes that evidence of an organic basis, though strong, is still circumstantial. As an example of an organic psychical condition, Symonds (1945) mentions a rare and restricted form of agnosia. The patient had a penetrating occipital wound, and presented with loss of perception of distance uncomplicated by other disabilities. But his odd behaviour, such as walking towards a wall with outstretched hands, led to an initial diagnosis of hysteria. He gave two examples of mental symptoms resulting from unlocalisable organic brain disease. Encephalitis, with its distinct pattern of intellectual impairment, persistent retrograde amnesia, and a gross defect of recent memory, is a similar clinical state to that seen after bilateral temporal lobe resection. A defect of moral sense is often found in children after encephalitis lethargica although it does not occur in adults, and Symonds infers that when learning has progressed to a certain stage before the onset of illness, behaviour is unaffected, in other words, the gross behavioural defect is caused by an insult during brain maturation. This 'moral agnosia', as Symonds aptly calls it, is accompanied by anti-social behaviour combined with skill in escaping detection.

Symonds also reviewed specific patterns of mental disorders caused by anti-psychotic medication such as Parkinsonism with oculogyric crises, or a schizophrenia-like psychosis precipitated by various hallucinogens, while anti-depressants may relieve a depressive illness, and conversely, *rauwolfia serpentina*, given to control hypertension, may precipitate psychotic depression.

Finally, Symonds suggests that if schizophrenia is, in fact, an organic brain disease, then a similar syndrome might be expected in some patients with cerebral tumours. He concedes that such cases would be rare and transient, owing to the increasing size of the tumour. Symonds did, in fact, report the case history of a patient with a glioblastoma, involving the corpus callosum and left frontal lobe, who presented with symptoms indistinguishable from schizophrenia. Two years previously the patient's sister had a left frontal tumour which also presented as a typical schizophrenic psychosis. He explained these genetically determined psychoses in Jacksonian terms, as release phenomena from the over-activity of healthy tissues below the lesion.

Denis Williams (1963) considered five psychological aspects of epilepsy beginning with brain damage affecting intellectual capacity, personality, and behaviour. Secondly, psychological stress suffered by epileptics through being different from their fellows and having to lead a more restrictive life. Thirdly, treatment may at times cause patients to become retarded or drowsy. Fourthly, disintegration by epilepsy of a life pattern causes a secondary neurosis often characterised by paranoid aggression, emotional instability, and severe mood changes. Finally when fits become more frequent they may mask an underlying affective state or various visceral stress disorders.

Among other neurological observations are those causing a disturbance in the sense of reality. Whitty and Lewin (1957) found that eight out of ten post-cingulectomy patients experienced increased vividness of thoughts, dreams, and fantasies. Patients had difficulty in distinguishing between mental events and happenings in the external environment, and were uncertain, for example, as to whether an event had actually occurred, or they had merely thought about it. Later, Whitty and Lewin (1960) explained this unusual form of confusional state as a Korsakoff type of amnesia-confabulatory syndrome representing a failure to organise remembered events in their temporal sequence: they believe that it is related to areas in the brain concerned with memory and emotions as delineated by Papez (1937). But this confusional state readily lends itself to a Jacksonian interpretation. It will be recalled that in healthy mentation Jackson believed that there is a rhythm of subjective and objective states with increased ideation, and proportionally less perception, while greater perception is accompanied by less ideation. But in this confusional state there is a reversal of healthy mentation and subjective images subconsciously precede objective ones. Thus a reduction in the rhythm of mentation to a lower, more organised and automatic level results in a defect of object consciousness with increased subject consciousness so that subjective images now appear real. Viewed from another aspect, a dissolution such as a cingulectomy causes loss of independence of the highest centres accompanied by increased innervation of lower ones. Thus, in a healthy state a 'faint' image aroused by thinking about something is, in this confusional state, replaced by a vivid image and the patient's sense of reality is disturbed.

One of the few British psychiatrists to apply Jacksonian principles is Thomas Power (1945, 1950, 1955, 1957, 1965) in his observations on the motor and mental manifestations accompanying therapeutically induced insulin coma and epilepsy. The inducement of an insulin coma supports Jackson's evolutionary principles of reduction from the voluntary to the involuntary, from the complex to the simple, and from highly differentiated to less differentiated or more stereotyped movements. In deepening coma localized movements are replaced by mass ones regarded by Power as signifying reduction towards the foetal level. His psychological investigations were hindered, to some extent, by the patient's amnesia; nevertheless 22 out of 100 did remember their experiences, which were similar to the 'reminiscences' described by Jackson and came withing the following themes: (a) reliving some episodes of their past (b) starting life afresh (c) being babies again (d) evolving again. In hypoglycaemia, nervous function is reduced to an ontogenetically earlier level; the mind also recaptures earlier experiences and focuses on events occurring around the beginning of life.

In the post-ictal state in 430 major fits induced by cardiazol in 110 patients, Power (1957) recognised three main thought patterns: the recapitulation of foetal behaviour, frequent repetitions, and the fusion of movements in mental and motor spheres. And he believes that these tendencies are directed towards functional unification or increased homogeneity.

In his final summary of the effects of insulin coma and drug-induced epilepsy, Power (1965) attempted to bridge the gulf between the mental and physical worlds. Psychological regression and nervous dissolution are, he believes, dynamic reactions to internal or external stress involving telescoping of the present into the distant past. Other common features are repetitions, perseverations, tonic innervations, states of muscular rigidity, and convulsive spasms. In organic brain lesions, repetitions are manifested in psychical, psychomotor, or motor spheres, and are related to the severity of the cerebral disturbances: they are also seen in such chronic conditions as the senile dementias and the post-encephalitic syndrome. Power also found that some patients expressed a blurring of the boundaries of self. Seventeen out of 119 patients expressed feelings of unreality and some believed the differences between themselves and others had been obliterated. He regards diminished awareness of self as a regressive phenomenon comparable to other psychoanalytical mechanisms such as projection, introjection, and identification.

Power considers that this is a parallel between psychoanalytical regression, and such organic mental disorders as senile dementia with a subjective "de-differentiation" in the dimension of time and space.

Other psychiatrists who have applied Jacksonian principles are F. L. Golla, Eliot Slater, and Erwin Stengel, while G. E. Berrios (1977) has discussed Jackson's theory of obsessional-compulsive states in relation to Henri Ey's organo-dynamic psychiatry, with regard to whose writings a particularly useful contribution has been made by Philip Evans (1972). In a discussion of temporal lobe epilepsy, Dewhurst and Beard (1970) have considered post-ictal confusional states in Jacksonian terms; and a patient with an organic brain lesion presenting as Capgras syndrome was discussed by Todd *et al.* (1981) as a phylogenetic regression to a less sophisticated mode of thought. But with these exceptions, few British psychiatrists have adopted Jacksonian principles. Recently, however, the wheel has come full circle through the reintroduction by Wing (1978) and Crow (1980 and 1981) of negative and positive symptoms in schizophrenia. But Freeman (1982) has rightly drawn attention to the possibility of confusion with Jackson's earlier use. This general neglect of Hughlings Jackson's writings is the main reason for this survey, and a secondary one is the fact that a study of Jacksonian principles is an essential prelude to the understanding of Henri Ey's organo-dynamic psychiatry.

Bibliography

Adrian, E. D., 'General principles of nervous activity', *Brain*, 1947, **70**, pp. 1–17.

Alajouanine, Th., 'Baillarger and Jackson: the principle of Baillarger–Jackson in aphasia', *J. Neurol. Neurosurg. & Psychiat.*, 1960, **23**, pp. 191–3.

Allen, O., *History of the York Dispensary*, York, 1845.

Amacher, Peter, *Freud's Neurological Education and its Influence*, Psychological Issues Monograph **16**, New York, 1965, pp. 19–20, 58–60.

Anderson, James, 'On sensory epilepsy. A case of basal cerebral tumour, affecting the left temporo-sphenoidal lobe, and giving rise to a paroxysmal taste-sensation and dreamy state', *Brain*, 1887, **9**, pp. 385–95.

Anderson, J., 'Epilepsies and Insanities' in *A Dictionary of Psychological Medicine*, ed. D. Hack Tuke, London 1892, **1**, pp. 440–50.

Angel, R. W., 'Jackson, Freud and Sherrington on the relation of brain and mind', *Amer. J. Psychiat.*, 1961, **118**, pp. 193–7.

Anon, 'Clinical and physiological researches on the nervous system', *J. of Psychol. Med.*, 1876, N.S. 2, pp. 150–5.

Anstie, F. E., *Stimulants and Narcotics, their Mutual Relations: with Special Researches on the Action of Alcohol, Aether and Chloroform, on the Vital Organism*, London, 1864.

Bailey, Pearce, 'The problem of temporal lobe epilepsy — purpose of colloquium' in *Temporal Lobe Epilepsy*, ed. M. Baldwin and P. Bailey, Springfield, Illinois, 1958, pp. 7–12.

Bartlet, J. E. A., 'Chronic psychosis following epilepsy', *Amer. J. Psychiat.*, 1957, **114**, pp. 338–43.

Bear, D. M. and Fedio, P., 'Quantitative analysis of inter-ictal behavior in temporal lobe epilepsy', *Arch. Neurol.*, 1977, **34**, pp. 454–7.

Beard, A. W. and Slater, E., 'The schizophrenia-like psychoses of epilepsy', *Proc. Roy. Soc. Med.*, 1962, **55**, pp. 311–16.

Benedek, L., 'On the life and works of Hughlings Jackson', *Clin. Nerv. & Ment. Dis.*, Debrecen, 1935, pp. 1–9.

Berrios, G. E., 'Henri Ey, Jackson et les idées obsédantes', *Évolut. psychiat.*, 1977, **42**, pp. 685–99.

Berrios, G. E., 'Insanity and epilepsy in the nineteenth century' in *Psychiatry, Genetics and Pathology. A Tribute to Eliot Slater*, ed. M. Roth and V. Cowie, London, 1979, pp. 161–71.

Berrios, G. E., 'Delirium and confusion in the 19th century. A conceptual history', *Brit. J. of Psychiat.*, 1981, **139**, pp. 439–49.

Bianchi, L., *Trattato di psichiatria*, Naples, 1905.

Bilikiewicz, T. and Lyskanowski, M., 'Poland' in *World History of Psychiatry*, ed. J. G. Howells, London, 1975, pp. 333–52.

Binswanger, L., 'Freud und die Verfassung der klinischen Psychiatrie', *Schweiz. Arch. Neur. Psychiat.*, 1936, **37**, pp. 177–99.

Blandford, G. F., *Insanity and its Treatment*, Edinburgh, 1871, p. 59.

Brain, W. R., 'Epilepsy', *Postgrad. Med. J.*, 1935, **11**, pp. 145–9.

Brain, W. R., 'Hughlings Jackson — A centenary memoir', *Lond. Hosp. Gaz.*, May 1935.

Brain, W. R., *Mind, Perception and Science*, Oxford, 1951.

Brain, W. R., 'The physiological basis of consciousness', *Brain*, 1958, **81**, pp. 420–55.

Brain, W. R., 'Neurology; past, present and future', *Brit. Med. J.*, 1958, 1, pp. 355–60.

Brain, W. R., 'Hughlings Jackson's ideas of consciousness in the light of today' in *The Brain and its Functions*, ed. F. N. L. Poynter, 1958, pp. 83–91.

Brain, W. R., 'The neurological tradition of the London Hospital or the importance of being thirty', *Lancet*, 1959, 2, pp. 578–81.

Brain, Lord, 'Some reflections on brain and mind' (Hughlings Jackson Lecture, M.N.I.), *Brain*, 1963, 86, pp. 381–402.

Bramwell, E., 'Hughlings Jackson Centenary. A commemorative dinner', *Brit. Med. J.*, 1935, 1, pp. 769–70.

Broadbent, Sir W., 'Hughlings Jackson as pioneer in nervous physiology', *Brain*, 1903, 26, pp. 21–36.

Bucknill, J. C. and Tuke, D. H., 'A manual of psychological medicine', London, 1858 and 1874, 1st and 3rd eds.

Buzzard, Sir E. Farquhar, 'Hughlings Jackson and his influence on neurology', *Lancet*, 1934, 2, pp. 909–13.

Carpenter, W. B., 'Principles of human physiology', London, 1842, 4th ed.; 1855, 5th ed.

Charcot, J.-M., 'Discussion on brain surgery', *Brit. Med. J.*, 1886, 2, pp. 674–5.

Clark, R. W., *Freud. The Man and the Cause*, London, 1980, p. 120.

Clarke, E. and O'Malley, C. D., *The Human Brain and Spinal Cord*, Berkeley and Los Angeles, 1968.

Clouston, T. S., *Clinical Lectures on Mental Diseases*, London, 1883.

Cobb, S., 'Consciousness and cerebral localization', *Epilepsia* (3rd series), 1952, 1, pp. 17–20.

Collier, J., 'Inventions and the outlook in neurology', *Lancet*, 1934, 2, pp. 855–9.

Crichton-Browne, J., ed., *W. Riding Lunatic Asylum Med. Reports*, 1871, 1, pref. p. iii.

Crichton-Browne, J., ed., *W. Riding Lunatic Asylum Med. Reports*, 1875, 5, pref. p. vi.

Critchley, M., 'Hughlings Jackson, the man, and the early days of the National Hospital', *Proc. Roy. Soc. Med.*, 1960, 53, pp. 613–18.

Critchley, M., 'The contributions of John Hughlings Jackson to neurology', *Cereb. Palsy Bull.*, 1960, 2, pp. 7–9.

Critchley, M., 'Jacksonian ideas and the future with special reference to aphasia', *Brit. Med. J.*, 1960, 2, pp. 6–12.

Critchley, M., 'Asphasiology and other aspects of language', London, 1970.

Crow, T. J., 'Positive and negative schizophrenic symptoms and the role of dopamine', *Brit. J. Psychiat.*, 1980, 137, pp. 383–6.

Crow, T. J., 'Positive and negative schizophrenic symptoms and the role of dopamine', *Brit. J. Psychiat.*, 1981, 139, pp. 251–4.

Currie, S., Heathfield, K. W. G., Henson, R. A., and Scott, D. F., 'Clinical course and prognosis of temporal lobe epilepsy: A survey of 666 patients', *Brain*, 1971, 94, pp. 173–90.

Delay, J., 'Le jacksonisme et l'œuvre de Ribot' in *Études de psychologie médicale*, Paris, 1953.

De Jong, R. N., 'Psychomotor or "temporal lobe" epilepsy: A review of the development of our present concept', *Neurol.*, 1957, 7, pp. 1–14.

De Jong, R. N., *A History of American Neurology*, New York, 1982.

Dewhurst, K. and Beard, A. W., 'Sudden religious conversions in temporal lobe epilepsy', *Brit. J. Psychiat.*, 1970, 117, pp. 497–507.

Dongier, S., 'Statistical study of clinical and electroencephalographic manifestations of 536 psychotic episodes occurring in 516 epileptics between clinical seizures', *Epilepsia* (Amsterdam), 1959–60, 1, pp. 117–42.

'Drewitt, Frederick George Dawtrey', *Lives of the Fellows of the Royal College of Physicians of London 1826–1925*, compiled by G. H. Brown, London, 1955, pp. 327–8.

Driver, M. V., 'Electroencephalography and the diagnosis of

temporal lobe disease' in *Modern Trends in Psychological Medicine*, ed. J. H. Price, 1970, pp. 326–45.

Ellenberger, Henri F., *The Discovery of the Unconscious. The History and Evolution of Dynamic Psychiatry*, London, 1970, p. 403.

Engelhardt, H. T., Jr, 'John Hughlings Jackson and the concept of cerebral localization', M.D. Thesis, Tulane University, New Orleans, 1972.

Engelhardt, H. T., Jr, 'John Hughlings Jackson and the mind-body relationship', *Bull. Hist. Med.*, 1975, 49, pp. 137–51.

Evans, Philip, 'Henri Ey's concept of the organization of consciousness and its disorganization: an extension of Jacksonian theory', *Brain*, 1972, 95, pp. 413–40.

Ey, H., 'The reality of mental disease and the disease of reality', *Compreh. Psychiat.*, 1960, 1, pp. 2–7.

Ey, H., 'Hughlings Jackson and the organo-dynamic concept of psychiatry', *Amer. J. of Psychiat.*, 1962, pp. 673–82.

Ey, H., 'Disorders of consciousness in psychiatry' in *Handbook of Clinical Neurology*, ed. P. J. Vinker and G. W. Bruyn, Amsterdam and New York, 1964, Vol. 3, Ch. 7, pp. 112–36.

Falconer, M. A. and Taylor, D. C., 'Temporal lobe epilepsy: clinical features, pathology, diagnosis and treatment' in *Modern Trends in Psychological Medicine*, ed. J. H. Price, 1970, pp. 346–73.

Falret, J., *Des maladies mentales et des asiles d'aliénés*, Paris, 1864.

Feindel, W. and Penfield, W., 'Localization of discharge in temporal lobe automatism', *A.M.A. Arch. Neurol. & Psychiat.*, 1954, 72, pp. 605–30.

Feindel, W., 'Response patterns elicited from the amygdala and deep temporoinsular cortex' in *Electrical Stimulation of the Brain*, ed. D. E. Sheer, Univ. Texas, Austin, 1961, pp. 87–106.

Feindel, W., 'Temporal lobe seizures' in *Handbook of Clinical Neurology*, ed. P. J. Vinker and G. W. Bruyn, Amsterdam and New York, 1974, 15, pp. 87–106.

Fenton, G. W., 'Epilepsy and automatism' in *Contemporary Psychiatry*, ed. T. Silverstone and B. Barraclough, London, 1975, pp. 429–39.

Ferrier, David, *The Functions of the Brain*, London, 1886, 2nd ed.

Ferrier, D., 'John Hughlings Jackson 1835–1911', *Proc. Roy. Soc.* (Series B), 1912, **84**, pp. xviii–xxv.

Flor-Henry, P., 'Psychosis and temporal lobe epilepsy', 1969, **10**, pp. 363–95.

Flor-Henry, P., 'Epilepsy and psychopathology' in *Recent Advances in Clinical Psychiatry*, ed. K. Granville-Grossman, Edinburgh, 2nd ed., 1976, pp. 262–95.

Forrest, D. W., *Francis Galton. The Life and Work of a Victorian Genius*, London, 1974.

Freeman, T., 'Positive and negative schizophrenic symptoms', *Brit. J. Psychiat.*, 1982, **140**, pp. 210–11.

Freud, S., *The Interpretation of Dreams* (first published 1900), London, 1953, p. 569n, 2nd part, Vol. V, Standard Edition.

Fritsch, G. and Hitzig, E., "Über die elektrische Erregbarkeit des Grosshirns", *Arch. Anst. Physiol. Wiss. Med.*, 1870, pp. 300–32.

Galton, F., 'Psychometric experiments', *Brain*, 1879, **2**, pp. 149–62.

Gaustaut, H., 'So-called "psychomotor" and "temporal epilepsy"', *Epilepsia*, 1953, **2**, pp. 59–96.

Gibbs, F. A., Gibbs, E. L., and Lennox, W. G., 'Epilepsy: a paroxysmal cerebral dysrhythmia', *Brain*, 1937, **60**, pp. 377–88.

Gibbs, F. A., Gibbs, E. L., and Lennox, W. G., 'Cerebral dysrhythmias of epilepsy', *Arch. Neurol. & Psychiat.*, 1938, **38**, 289–314.

Gibbs, F. A., Gibbs, E. L., and Lennox, W. G., 'The likeness of the cortical dysrhythmias of schizophrenia and psychomotor epilepsy', *Amer. J. of Psychiat.*, 1938, **95**, pp. 255–69.

Gibbs, E. L., Gibbs, F. A, and Fuster, B., 'Psychomotor-epilepsy', *Arch. Neurol. & Psychiat.*, 1948, **60**, pp. 331–9.

Gilles de la Tourette, G., 'Étude sur une affection nerveuse caractérisée par de l'inco-ordination motrice accompagnée d'écholalie et de coprolalie (jumping latah myriachit)', *Arch. de neurol.*, 1885, **9**, pp. 19–42, 158–222.

Gloor, P., Olivier, A., and Quesney, L. F., 'The role of the amygdala in the expression of psychic phenomena in temporal lobe seizures', *I.N.S.E.R.M. Symposium* No. 20, 1981, pp. 489–98.

Golla, F., 'The objective study of the neurosis', *Lancet*, 1921, **2**, pp. 115–22.

Golla, F. L., review of *Selected Writings of John Hughlings Jackson*, ed. James Taylor, *J. Ment. Sci.*, 1932, **78**, pp. 204–6.

Gowers, W. R., *Epilepsy and other Chronic Convulsive Diseases*, London 1881, p. 217.

Gowers, W. R., *A Manual of Diseases of the Nervous System*, London, 1888, Vol. 2, p. 87.

Gowers, W. R., 'On special senses discharges from organic disease', *Brain*, 1909, **32**, pp. 303–26.

Greenblatt, S. H., 'The major influences on the early life and work of John Hughlings Jackson', *Bull. Hist. Med.*, 1965, **39**, pp. 346–76.

Greenblatt, S. H., 'Hughlings Jackson's first encounter with the work of Paul Broca: the physiological and philosophical background', *Bull. Hist. Med.*, 1970, **44**, pp. 555–70.

Grinker, R. R., 'A comparison of psychological "repression" and neurological inhibition', *J. Nerv. Ment. Dis.*, 1939, **89**, pp. 765–81.

Grinker, R. R., 'The interrelation of neurology, psychiatry and psychoanalysis', *J.A.M.A.*, 1941, **21**, pp. 2236–41.

Hamilton, A. M., *Nervous Diseases, their Description and Treatment*, London, 1878.

Hammond, W. A., *A Treatise on Diseases of the Nervous System*, New York, 1871 and 1881.

Handfield Jones, C., *Studies on Functional Nervous Disorders*, London, 1870.

Hare, E. H., 'Masturbatory insanity: The history of an idea', *J. Ment. Sci.*, 1962, **108**, pp. 1–25.

Harris, W., 'The Hughlings Jackson Memorial Lecture' (Privately printed for subscribers to Hughlings Jackson Memorial Lecture), 1932.

Harris, W., 'John Hughlings Jackson 1835–1911', *Postgrad. Med. J.*, 1935, **11**, pp. 131–4.

Haymaker, Webb, and Schiller, F., eds., *The Founders of Neurology*, 2nd ed., Springfield, Illinois, 1957.

Head, Henry, 'Certain mental changes that accompany visceral disease', The Goulstonian Lectures for 1901, London, pp. 1–85.

Head, Henry, 'Hughlings Jackson on aphasia and kindred affections of speech', *Brain*, 1915, **38**, pp. 1–27.

Head, Henry, 'Some principles of neurology', *Brain*, 1918, **41**, pp. 344–54.

Head, H., 'Aphasia: An historical review', *Brain*, 1920, **43**, pp. 390–411.

Head, H., 'Release of function in the nervous system', *Proc. Roy. Soc.*, 1921, **92**, pp. 184–209.

Hebb, D. O., 'Intelligence, brain function and the theory of mind' (Hughlings Jackson Lecture, M.N.I.), *Brain*, 1959, **82**, pp. 260–75.

Hill, D., 'Epilepsy: clinical aspects' in *Electroencephalogy*, eds. D. Hill and G. Parr, London, 1963, pp. 250–94.

Hill, D., 'Historical review' in *Epilepsy and Psychiatry*, eds. E. H. Reynolds and M. R. Trimble, Edinburgh/London/Melbourne/New York, 1981, pp. 1–11.

Holmes, G., *The National Hospital, Queen Square, 1860–1948*, Edinburgh and London, 1954.

Hunter, R. A. and Hurwitz, L. J., 'The case notes of the National Hospital for the Paralysed and Epileptic, Queen Square, London before 1900', *J. Neurol. Neurosurg. Psychiat.*, 1961, **24**, pp. 167–94.

Hunter, R. and Macalpine, I., *Three Hundred Years of Psychiatry 1535–1860*, London, 1963, p. 1080.

Hunter, R. and Macalpine, I., *Psychiatry for the Poor. 1851 Colney Hatch Asylum. Friern Hospital 1973. A Medical and Social History*, London, 1974.

Hutchinson, J., 'Recollections of a lifelong friendship', *Brit. Med. J.*, 1911, 2, p. 952.

Huxley, T. H., *Method and Results*, London, 1893, pp. 240–9.

Itard, J. M. T., 'Mémoire sur quelques fonctions involontaires des appareils de la voix', *Arch. gén. de méd.*, 1825, 8, pp. 385–407.

Jackson, J. Hughlings, 'Loss of speech and hemiplegia on the right side; recovery of power to swear', *Clin. Lect. and Reports to the London Hosp.*, 1864, 1, pp. 452–3.

Jackson, J. Hughlings, 'Involuntary ejaculations following fright — subsequently chorea', *Med. Times & Gaz.*, 1865, 1, p. 89.

Jackson, J. Hughlings, 'Observations on defects of sight in diseases of the nervous system', *Roy. Lond. Ophth. Hosp. Rep.*, 1865, 4, p. 389; 1866, 5, pp. 51, 251.

Jackson, J. Hughlings, 'Clinical remarks on the occasional occurence of subjective sensation of smell in patients who are liable to epileptiform seizures, or who have symptoms of mental derangement, and in others', *Lancet*, 1866, 1, pp. 659–60.

Jackson, J. Hughlings, 'Remarks on disorderly movements of chorea and convulsions', *Medical Times & Gaz.*, 1867, 2, pp. 642–3.

Jackson, J. Hughlings, 'A study of convulsions', *Trans. St. And. Med. Grad. Assoc.*, 1869, 3, pp. 162–204. Reprinted Odell and Ives, 1870, 45 pp.

Jackson, J. Hughlings, 'Remarks on the double condition of loss of consciousness and mental automatism following certain epileptic seizures', *Med. Times & Gaz.*, 1873, 2, pp. 63–4.

Jackson, J. Hughlings, 'On the anatomical and physiological localization of movements in the brain', *Lancet*, 1873, 1, pp. 84–5, 162–4. Reprinted J. & A. Churchill, London, 1875, 37 pp.

Jackson, J. Hughlings, 'Remarks on systemic sensations in epilepsies', *Brit. Med. J.*, 1874, **1**, p. 174.

Jackson, J. Hughlings, 'The comparative study of drunkenness', *Brit. Med. J.*, 1874, **1**, pp. 652–3, 685–6.

Jackson, J. Hughlings, 'On the scientific and empirical investigation of epilepsies', *Med. Press & Circ.*, 1874, **2**, pp. 325–7, 347–52, 389–92, 497–9, 519–21. *Med. Press & Circ.*, 1875, **1**, pp. 353–5, 397–400, 419–21; **2**, pp. 313–15, 355–8, 487–9. *Med. Press & Circ.*, 1876, **1**, pp. 63–5, 129–31, 173–6, 313–16.

Jackson, J. Hughlings, 'On temporary mental disorders after epileptic paroxysms', *W. Riding Lunatic Asylum Med. Reports*, 1875, **5**, pp. 105–29.

Jackson, J. Hughlings, 'Nervous symptoms in cases of congenital syphilis', *J. Ment. Sci.*, 1875, **20**, pp. 517–27.

Jackson, J. Hughlings, 'Intellectual warnings of epileptic seizures', *Med. Times & Gaz.*, 1876, **2**, p. 702.

Jackson, J. Hughlings, 'On epilepsies and on the after-effects of epileptic discharges (Todd & Robertson's hypothesis)', *W. Riding Asylum Med. Reports*, 1876, **6**, pp. 266–309.

Jackson, J. Hughlings, 'On affections of speech from disease of the brain': first paper, *Brain*, 1878/9, **1**, pp. 304–30; second paper, *Brain*, 1879/80, **2**, pp. 203–22, 323–56.

Jackson, J. Hughlings, 'Lectures on the diagnosis of epilepsy' (Delivered before the Harveian Society), *Med. Times & Gaz.*, 1879, **1**, pp. 29–33, 85–8, 141–3, 223–6.

Jackson, J. Hughlings, 'Psychology and the nervous system', *Med. Press & Circ.*, 1879, **2**, pp. 199–201, 239–41, 283–5, 409–11, 429–30.

Jackson, J. Hughlings, 'On right- or left-sided spasm at the onset of epileptic paroxysms, and on crude sensation, warnings and elaborate mental states', *Brain*, 1880/1, **3**, pp. 192–206.

Jackson, J. Hughlings, 'On temporary paralysis after epileptiform and epileptic seizures; a contribution to the study of dissolution of the nervous system', *Brain*, 1881, **3**, pp. 433–51.

Jackson, J. Hughlings, 'Remarks on dissolutions of the nervous system as exemplified by certain post-epileptic conditions', *Med. Press & Circ.*, 1881, **31**, pp. 329–32, 399; **32**, pp. 68–70, 380–9.

Jackson, J. Hughlings, 'An address delivered at the opening meeting of the section of pathology at the annual meeting of the British Medical Association, in Worcester, August 1882', *Brit. Med. J.*, 1882, **2**, pp. 305–8.

Jackson, J. Hughlings, 'Evolution and dissolution of the nervous system' (Croonian Lectures), *Brit. Med. J.*, 1884, **1**, pp. 591, 660, 703; *Med. Times & Gaz.*, 1884, **1**, pp. 411, 445, 485; *Lancet*, 1884, **1**, pp. 535–55, 649, 739.

Jackson, J. Hughlings, 'Discussion on brain surgery', *Brit. Med. J.*, 1886, **2**, pp. 674–5.

Jackson, J. Hughlings, 'An address on the psychology of joking', *Brit. Med. J.*, 1887, **2**, pp. 870–1; *Lancet*, 1887, **2**, p. 800; *Proc. Med. Soc. Lond.*, 1888, **11**, p. 1.

Jackson, J. Hughlings, 'Remarks on evolution and dissolution of the nervous system', *J. Ment. Sci.*, 1887, **33**, pp. 25–48; *Med. Press & Circ.*, 1887, N.S., **44**, pp. 2, 461, 491, 511, 586, 617. Reprinted J. Bale & Son, London, 1888, 8°, 40 pp.

Jackson, J. Hughlings, 'On post-epileptic states. A contribution to the comparative study of insanities', *J. Ment. Sci.*, 1888, **34**, pp. 349–65, 490–500; **35**, pp. 145–7. Reprinted Lewes H. Wolff, London, 1888, 8°, 17 pp.

Jackson, J. Hughlings, 'Remarks on the diagnosis and treatment of diseases of the brain', *Brit. Med. J.*, 1888, **2**, pp. 59, 111.

Jackson, J. Hughlings, 'On the comparative study of diseases of the nervous system', *Brit. Med. J.*, 1889, **2**, pp. 355–62.

Jackson, J. Hughlings, 'On a particular variety of epilepsy ("intellectual aura"), one case with symptoms of organic brain disease', *Brain*, 1888, **11**, pp. 179–207.

Jackson, J. Hughlings and Beevor, C. E., 'Case of tumour of the right temporo-sphenoidal lobe, bearing on the localisation of the sense of smell and on the interpretation of a particular variety of epilepsy', *Brain*, 1889/90, 12, pp. 346–57.

Jackson, J. Hughlings, 'Lecture on neurological fragments' (Lecture to Hunterian Society 1892), *Lancet*, 1892, 1, pp. 511–14; *Brit. Med. J.*, 1892, 1, pp. 487–92. Reprinted in *Neurological Fragments by John Hughlings Jackson*, with biographical memoir by James Taylor, Oxford, 1925.

Jackson, J. Hughlings, 'Words and other symbols in mentation', *Med. Press & Circ.*, 1893, 107, pp. 205–8.

Jackson, J. Hughlings, 'The factors of insanities', *Med. Press & Circ.*, 1894, N.S., 57, pp. 615–19.

Jackson, J. Hughlings, 'On imperative ideas', *Brain*, 1895, 18, p. 318.

Jackson, J. Hughlings, 'Relations of different divisions of the central nervous system to one another and to parts of the body', *Lancet*, 1898, 1, pp. 79–87.

Jackson, J. H. and Colman, W. S., 'Case of epilepsy with tasting movements and "dreamy" state: very small patch of softening in the left uncinate gyrus', *Brain*, 1898, 21, pp. 589–90.

Jackson, J. Hughlings, 'On asphyxia in slight epileptic paroxysms. On the symptomatology of slight epileptic fits supposed to depend on discharge-lesions of the uncinate gyrus', *Lancet*, 1899, 1, pp. 79–80.

Jackson, J. H. and Stewart, J. P., 'Epileptic attacks with a warning of a crude sensation of smell and intellectual aura (dreamy state) in a patient who had symptoms pointing to gross organic disease of the right temporo-sphenoidal lobe', *Brain*, 1899, 22, pp. 534–99.

Janet, Pierre, 'Les obsessions et la psychasthénie', Paris, 1903.

Janet, Pierre, *Centenaire de Théodule Ribot. Jubilé de la psychologie française*, Paris, 1939.

Jasper, H. H., 'Functional subdivisions of the temporal region in relation to seizure patterns and subcortical connections' in *Temporal Lobe Epilepsy*, ed. M. Baldwin and P. Bailey, Springfield, Illinois, 1958, pp. 40–57.

Jasper, H. H., 'Evolution of concepts and cerebral localization since Hughlings Jackson' (Hughlings Jackson Lecture, M.N.I., 1959), *World Neurol.*, 1960, 1, pp. 97–111.

Jelliffe, S. E. and White, W. A., *Diseases of the Nervous System. A Text-book of Neurology and Psychiatry*, Philadelphia and New York, 1915.

Jefferson, G., 'Jacksonian epilepsy', *Postgrad. Med. J.*, 1935, 11, pp. 150–62.

Jones, Ernest, *Sigmund Freud. Life and Work*, London, 1953, Vol. I, p. 390.

Kaczyński, M., 'Dr Jan Mazurkiewicz — creator of Polish scientific psychiatry', *Psychiatria Polska*, 1975, 9, pp. 457–61.

Kennedy, F., 'John Hughlings Jackson', *Bull N.Y. Acad. Med.*, 1935, 11, pp. 479–80.

Langworthy, O. R., 'Hughlings Jackson — his opinion concerning epilepsy', *J. Nerv. & Ment. Dis.*, 1932, 76, pp. 574–85.

Lassek, A. M., Sr., 'The unique legacy of Dr Hughlings Jackson', Springfield, Illinois, 1970.

Lashley, K. S., 'Functional determinants of cerebral localization', *A.M.A. Arch. Neurol. Psychiat.*, 1937, 38, pp. 371–87.

Lashley, K. S., 'Factors limiting recovery of the central nervous lesions' (Hughlings Jackson Lecture, M.N.I., 1937), *J. Ner. Ment. Dis.*, 1938, 88, pp. 735–65.

Laycock, T., *A Treatise on the Nervous Diseases of Women*, London, 1840.

Laycock, Thomas, 'On the reflex function of the brain', *Brit. & For. Med. Rev.*, 1845, Jan., pp. 298–311.

Laycock, T., *The Principles of Physiology, by John Augustus Unzer, and a Dissertation on the Functions of the Nervous System, by George Prochaska*, (transl. ed.), The Sydenham Society, London, 1851.

Laycock, T., *Mind and Brain: or, the Correlations of Consciousness and Organisation, with the Application to Philosophy, Zoology, Physiology, Mental Pathology, and the Practice of Medicine*, 2 vols., Edinburgh, 1860.

'Laycock, T.', *Dictionary of National Biography*, ed. S. Lee, 1909, 11, pp. 744–5.

Lennox, W. G. and Lennox, M. A., *Epilepsy and Related Disorders*, 2 vols., London, 1960.

Levin, K., *Freud's Early Psychology of the Neuroses*, Pittsburg, 1978.

Levin, M., 'The basic symptoms of schizophrenia', *Amer. J. Psychiat.*, 1931, 11, pp. 215–36.

Levin, M., 'Bromide delirium and other bromide psychoses', *Amer. J. Psychiat.*, 1933, 89, pp. 1128–58.

Levin, M., 'Hughlings Jackson's views on mentation. Their value for the psychiatrist', *Arch. Neurol. Psychiat.*, 1933, 30, pp. 848–74.

Levin, M., 'Elaborate mental states after slight epileptic paroxysms', *A.M.A. Arch. Neurol. Psychiat.*, 1934, 32, pp. 397–400.

Levin, M., 'Hughlings Jackson's views on degrees of automatic action, as applied to a case of catatonia', *Amer. J. Psychiat.*, 1934/5, 91, pp. 109–12.

Levin, M., 'On the causation of mental symptoms: an inquiry into the psychiatric application of Hughlings Jackson's views on the causation of nervous symptoms, with particular references to their application to delirium and schizophrenia', *J. Ment. Ner. Dis.*, 1936, 72, pp. 11–27.

Levin, M., 'Degrees of automatic action: some psychiatric applications of Hughlings Jackson's concept of reduction to a more automatic condition', *J. Neurol. & Psychopathol.*, 1936, 17, p. 153.

Levin, M., 'The pathogenesis of hallucinations and delusions: remarks on the distinction between pathogenesis and etiology in psychiatry', *Arch. Neurol. & Psychiat.*, 1937, 37, pp. 839–47.

Levin, M., 'Misunderstanding of the pathogenesis of schizophrenia arising from the concept of splitting', *Amer. J. Psychiat.*, 1938, **94**, pp. 877–89.

Levin, M., 'The seeming aggravation of drug delirium after withdrawal of the drug and its bearing on the harmfulness of withdrawal', *Amer. J. Psychiat.*, 1938, **95**, pp. 697–700.

Levin, M., 'Reconstruction of dreams', *Amer. J. Psychiat.*, 1939, **96**, pp. 705–10.

Levin, M., 'Inability in delirium to name the physician's vocation on command, with retention of the ability to name it spontaneously: an illustration of Hughlings Jackson's law of reduction to a more automatic condition', *J. Ment. Sci.*, 1939, **85**, pp. 1043–6.

Levin, M., 'Delirious disorientation: the law of the unfamiliar mistaken for the familiar', *J. Ment. Sci.*, 1945, **91**, pp. 447–53.

Levin, M., 'Partial or incomplete delirium', *J.A.M.A.*, 1945, **129**, p. 610.

Levin, M., 'Delirium: a gap in psychiatric teaching', *Amer. J. Psychiat.*, 1951, **107**, pp. 689–94.

Levin, M., 'Reflex action in the highest cerebral centres. A tribute to Hughlings Jackson', *J. Nerv. & Ment. Dis*, 1953, **118**, pp. 481–93.

Levin, M., 'The mind–brain problem and Hughlings Jackson's doctrine of concomitance', *Amer. J. Psychiat.*, 1960, **116**, pp. 718–22.

Levin, M., 'The levels of the nervous system and their capacity to function independently of each other', *J. Nerv. Ment. Dis.*, 1962, **132**, pp. 75–9.

Levin, M., 'Nature of psychiatric research, with reflection on research of Freud and Hughlings Jackson and on limitations of statistics', *Amer. J. Psychiat.*, 1962/3, **119**, pp. 404–9.

Levin, M., 'Our debt to Hughlings Jackson', *J.A.M.A.*, 1965, **191**, pp. 991–6.

Lief, A., *The Commonsense Psychiatry of Dr Adolf Meyer*, New York/Toronto/London, 1948.

López Piñero, J. M., *John Hughlings Jackson (1835–1911). Evolucionismo y Neurología*, Madrid, 1973.

Luria, A. R., *Higher Cortical Functions in Man*, London, 1966.

McEachern, D., 'John Hughlings Jackson 1835–1911', *A.M.A. Arch. Neurol. Psychiat.*, 1935, 33, pp. 636–42.

McHenry, L. C. and Lennox, W. G., ed., *Garrison's History of Neurology*, Springfield, Illinois, 1969.

Macnalty, Sir Arthur, 'Some pioneers of the past in neurology', *Med. Hist.*, 1965, 9, pp. 249–59.

Manacéïne, M. de, *Sleep: Its Physiology, Pathology and Psychology*, London, 1897.

Martin, J. Purdon, 'The discharging lesion in neurology', *Brain*, 1945, 68, pp. 167–86.

Martin, J. Purdon, 'Consciousness and its disturbances', *Lancet*, 1949, 1, pp. 48–53.

Martin, J. Purdon, 'Neurology in fiction: the turn of the screw', *Brit. Med. J.*, 1973, 2, pp. 717–21.

Martin, J. Purdon, 'Kinnier Wilson's notes on conversations with Hughlings Jackson', *J. Neurol. Neurosurg. & Psychiat.*, 1975, 38, pp. 313–16.

Maudsley, H., *The Pathology of Mind*, London, 1879.

Maurice-Williams, R. S., 'The achievements of Hughlings Jackson', *St. Thomas Hosp. Gaz.*, 1967, 65, pp. 43–51.

Mazurkiewicz, J., 'Les intégrations nerveuses', *Arch. Internat. de Neurol.*, 1935, 54, pp. 167–97.

Mazurkiewicz, J., 'Wstęp do psychofizjologii normalnej', Warsaw, 1950.

Menninger, K., Ellenberger, H., Pruyser, P. and Mayman, M., 'The unitary concept of mental illness', *Bull. Menn. Clinic*, 1958, 22, pp. 4–12.

Mercier, C., 'The late Dr Hughlings Jackson', *Brit. Med. J.*, 1912, 1, pp. 85–6. Reprinted in *Recollections*, 1925.

Meyer, A., *Psychobiology: a Science of Man*, Springfield, Illinois, 1957.

Mills, C. K., 'The evolution of our knowledge of the brain

during the last sixty years: illustrated with a series of personal observations' (Read at Philadelphia Neurological Society, 25 March 1927), *Arch. Neurol. Psychiat.*, 1927, **18**, pp. 832–45.

Milner, B., 'On the duality of the brain' (Hughlings Jackson Lecture, M.N.I.), 1979 (unpublished).

Mitchell, S. Weir, 'Some of the lessons of neurotomy', *Brain*, 1878, **1**, pp. 287–303.

Mitchell, S. Weir, *Lectures on Diseases of the Nervous System, Especially in Women*, Philadelphia, 1881.

Monakow, C. von and Mourgue, R., *Introduction biologique à l'étude de la neurologie et de la psychopathologie, intégration et désintégration de la fonction*, Paris, 1928.

Monro, H., 'Remarks on insanity: its nature and treatment', Pt. I, London, 1850. Reprinted with Pt. II, London, 1851.

Muskens, L. J. J., *Epilepsy. Comparative Pathogenesis, Symptoms, Treatment*, London, 1928.

Myers, A. T., 'A case of Raynaud's disease', *Tr. Clin. Soc. Lond.*, 1885, **8**, pp. 336–8.

Myers, A. T. and Whipman, T., 'On some chronic nervous sequelae of smallpox especially affecting the speech', *Tr. Clin. Soc. Lond.*, 1886, **19**, pp. 164–89.

Myers, A. T., 'A medical index-catalogue of the Library of the Surgeon General's Office, U.S. Army, Vol. VII — Insignares–Leghorn', *Nature*, 1886/7, **35**, p. 196.

Myers, A. T., 'Hypnotism at home and abroad', *The Practitioner*, 1890, **44**, pp. 196–206.

Myers, A. T. and Myers, F. W. H., 'Mind-cure, faith-cure and the miracles of Lourdes', *Proc. Soc. Psych. Res.*, 1893, **9**, pp. 160–209.

'Myers. A. T.', *Lives of the Fellows of the Royal College of Physicians of London 1826–1925*, compiled by G. H. Brown, London, 1955, pp. 365–6.

Myers, F. W. H., Podmore, F. and Gurney, E., *Phantasms of the Living*, 2 vols., London, 1886.

Myers, F. W. H., 'The subliminal self', *Proc. Soc. for Psych. Res.*, 1895, 11, pp. 334–51, 585–93.

Myers, F. W. H., *Human Personality and its Survival of Bodily Death*, 2 vols., London, 1903.

'Myers, F. W. H.', *Dictionary of National Biography*, (Supplement ed. S. Lee), 1909, 22, pp. 1087–90.

Nielsen, J. M. and Thompson, G. N., *The Engrammes of Psychiatry*, Springfield, Illinois, 1947, pp. 59–60.

O'Leary, J. L. and Goldring, J., *Science and Epilepsy*, New York, 1976, pp. 91–5.

Papez, J. W., 'Proposed mechanism of emotion', *Arch. Neurol. & Psychiat.*, 1937, 38, pp. 725–43.

Parker, H. L., 'Jacksonian convulsions: an historical note', *The Journal Lancet*, 1929, 49, pp. 107–11.

Penfield, W. and Rasmussen, T., 'The cerebral cortex of man', New York, 1950.

Penfield, W., 'Temporal lobe epilepsy' (Hunterian Lecture), *Brit. J. Surg.*, 1954, 41, pp. 337–43.

Penfield, W., 'The role of the temporal cortex in certain psychological phenomena', *J. Ment. Sci.*, 101, pp. 451–65.

Penfield, W., 'The brain's record of experience: auditory and visual' (Hughlings Jackson lecture 1961, M.N.I.), expanded and published with P. Perot as 'The Brain's recording of auditory and visual experience. A final summary and conclusion', *Brain*, 1963, 86, pp. 595–702.

Pick, A., *Die agrammatischen Sprachstörungen*, Prague, 1913.

Podmore, F., *Apparitions and Thought Transference: an Examination of the Evidence of Telepathy*, London, 1894.

Podolsky, E., 'Hughlings Jackson and the thinking machine', *Med. Rec.*, 1947, 160, pp. 676–8.

Pond, D. A., 'Psychiatric aspects of epilepsy', *J. Indian Med. Prof.*, 1957, 3, pp. 1441–51.

Power, T. D., 'Psychosomatic regression in therapeutic epilepsy', *Psychosom. Med.*, 1945, 7, pp. 279–90.

Power, T. D., 'The problem of the therapeutic convulsion', *Brit. Med. J.*, 1950, **2**, pp. 1092–4.

Power, T. D., 'Reversal of evolution in insulin coma', *J. Nerv. Ment. Dis.*, 1955, **121**, pp. 535–44.

Power, T. D., 'A psychiatrist looks at epilepsy', *J. Ment. Nerv. Dis.*, 1957, **125**, pp. 279–92.

Power, T. D., 'Some aspects of brain–mind relationship', *Brit. J. Psychiat.*, 1965, **111**, pp. 1215–23.

Prince, M., 'Hughlings Jackson on the connection between the mind and the brain', *Brain*, 1891, **14**, pp. 250–69.

Putnam, J. J., 'Certain features of the work of the late J. Hughlings Jackson', *Boston Med. Surg. J.*, 1913, **169**, pp. 73–6.

Putnam, J. J., *Human Motives*, New York, 1915.

Quaerens (A. T. Myers), 'A prognosis and therapeutic indication in epilepsy', *Practitioner*, 1874, **8**, pp. 284–5.

Reynolds, J. R., *Epilepsy: its Symptoms, Treatment and Relation to Other Chronic Convulsive Diseases*, London, 1861.

Ribot, Th., *La psychologie anglaise contemporaine*, Paris, 1870.

Ribot, Th., *Les maladies de la mémoire*, Paris, 1881.

Ribot, Th., *Les maladies de la volonté*, Paris, 1883.

Ribot, Th., *Les maladies de la personnalité*, Paris, 1885.

Riese, W., 'An outline of a history of ideas in neurology', *Bull. Hist. Med.*, 1949, **23**, pp. 111–36.

Riese, W., 'Hughlings Jackson's doctrine of consciousness. Sources, versions and elaborations', *J. Nerv. & Ment. Dis.*, 1954, **120**, pp. 330–7.

Riese, W., 'Hughlings Jackson's doctrine of aphasia and its significance today', *J. Nerv. & Ment. Dis.*, 1955, **122**, pp. 11–13.

Riese, W., and Gooddy, W., 'An original clinical record of Hughlings Jackson with an interpretation', *Bull. Hist. Med.*, 1955, **29**, pp. 230–8.

Riese, W., 'The source of Jacksonian neurology', *J. Nerv. & Ment. Dis.*, 1956, **124**, pp. 125–34.

Riese, W., 'Freudian concepts of brain function and brain disease', *J. Nerv. & Ment. Dis.*, 1958, **127**, pp. 287–307.

Riese, W., 'The sources of Hughlings Jackson's view of aphasia', *Brain*, 1965, **88**, pp. 811–22.

Riese, W., 'Changing concepts of cerebral localization', *Clio Medica*, 1967, **2**, pp. 189–230.

Rouart, J., 'Janet et Jackson', *Évolut. psychiat.*, 1950, **3**, pp. 485–6.

Sachs, B., 'On arrested cerebral development with special reference to its cortical pathology', *J. Nerv. Ment. Dis.*, 1887, **13**, pp. 541–53.

Sachs, E., 'Reminiscences of an American student', *Brit. Med. J.*, 1957, **1**, pp. 916–17.

Savage, G. H. and Goodall, E., *Insanity and Allied Neuroses*, 4th ed., London, 1907, p. 68.

Savage, Sir G., 'Hughlings Jackson on mental disorders', *J. Ment. Sci.*, 1917, **63**, pp. 315–28.

Schaltenbrand, G., 'Hughlings Jackson', *Münch. Mediz. Wochn.*, 1936, **146**, pp. 1–8.

Schiller, F., 'Consciousness reconsidered', *A.M.A. Arch. Neurol. Psychiat.*, 1952, **67**, pp. 199–227.

Sequin, E. C., *Opera Minora. A Collection of Essays, Articles, Lectures and Addresses from 1866–1822 inclusive*, New York, 1884.

Sidgwick, H., Sidgwick, E. M., Myers, A. T., Podmore, F., Johnson, A. and Myers, F. W. H., 'Census of hallucinations', *Proc. Soc. Psych. Res.*, 1894, **10**, pp. 25–422.

Sieveking, E. H., *On Epilepsy and Epileptiform Seizures*, London, 1858.

Sittig, O., *J. Hughlings Jackson's Eine Studie über Krämpfe*, Prague, 1926.

Skae, D., 'A rational and practical classification of insanity', *J. Ment. Sci.*, 1863, **9**, pp. 309–19.

Skae, D., 'The Morrisonian Lectures on insanity for 1873', ed. T. S. Clouston, *J. Ment. Sci.*, 1873, **19**, pp. 340–55.

Slater, E., Beard, A. W. and Glithero, E., 'The schizophrenia-like psychoses of epilepsy', *Brit. J. Psychiat.*, 1963, **109**, pp. 95–150.

Spillane, J. D., 'Hughlings Jackson's American contemporaries: the birth of American neurology', *Prec. Roy. Soc. Med.*, 1976, **69**, pp. 393–408.

Stengel, E., S. *Freud's* On Aphasia *(1891). A Critical Study*, London, 1953.

Stengel, E., 'A re-evaluation of Freud's book *On Aphasia*. Its significance for psycho-analysis', *Intern. J. Psychoanal.*, 1954, **35**, pp. 85–9.

Stengel, E., 'The origins and the status of dynamic psychiatry', *Brit. J. Med. Psychol.*, 1954, **27**, pp. 193–200.

Stengel, E., 'Hughlings Jackson's influence in psychiatry', 1963, *Brit. J. Psychiat.*, **109**, pp. 348–55.

Stewart, T. Grainger, obituary of Sir David Ferrier, *J. Ment. Sci.*, 1928, **74**, pp. 375–80.

Symonds, C. P., 'Discussion on the ocular sequelae of head injuries', *Trans. Ophthmal. Soc. U.K.*, 1945, **65**, pp. 3–19.

Symonds, C. P., 'Prognosis in closed head injuries', *Brit Med. Bull.*, 1945, **3**, pp. 14–18.

Symonds, C., 'Classification of epilepsies with particular reference to psychomotor seizures', *A.M.A. Arch. Neurol. Psychiat. (Chic.)*, 1954, **72**, pp. 631–7.

Symonds, C., 'Excitation and inhibition in epilepsy', *Brain*, 195?, **82**, pp. 133–45.

Symonds, C., 'Disease of mind and disorder of brain', *Brit. Med. J.*, 1960, **2**, pp. 1–5.

Symonds, C., 'Memory disorder following brain damage', expanded and published as 'Disorders of memory' (Hughlings Jackson Lecture, M.N.I.), *Brain*, 1966, **89**, pp. 625–44.

Talbott, J. H., 'John Hughlings Jackson (1835–1911)'. *A Biographical History of Medicine*, New York/London, 1970, pp. 830–2.

Taylor, D. C. and Marsh, S. M., 'Hughlings Jackson's Dr Z: the paradigm of temporal lobe epilepsy revealed', *J. Neurol. Neurosurg. & Psychiat.*, 1980, **43**, pp. 758–67.

Taylor, James, ed., *Neurological Fragments by Hughlings Jackson, with a Biographical Memoir*, Oxford Med. Publ., 1925.

Taylor, James, ed., *Selected Writings of John Hughlings Jackson*, 2 vols., London, 1931/2.

Temkin, O., *The Falling Sickness*, 1st ed. 1945, 2nd ed., Baltimore and London, 1971.

Thornton, E. M., *Hypnotism, Hysteria and Epilepsy. A Historical Synthesis*, London, 1976, pp. 53–65.

Todd, J., Dewhurst, K. and Wallace, G., 'The syndrome of Capgras', *Brit. J. of Psychiat.*, 1981, **139**, pp. 319–27.

Toone, B., 'Psychoses of epilepsy' in *Epilepsy and Psychiatry*, ed. E. H. Reynolds and M. R. Trimble, Edinburgh/London/Melbourne/New York, 1981, pp. 113–37.

'Tuke, D. H.', in *Lives of the Fellows of the Royal College of Physicians of London 1826–1926*, compiled by G. H. Brown, London, 1955, p. 237.

Van Gieson, I., 'A case of psycho-motor epilepsy' in *Semicentennial Volume of the American Neurological Association (1875–1924)*, New York, 1924, p. 345.

Viets, H. R., 'Hughlings Jackson (1835–1911)', *New Engl. J. of Med.*, 1931, **205**, pp. 17, 827–8.

Viets, H. R., 'West Riding 1871–1876', *Bull. Inst. Hist. Med.*, 1938, **6**, pp. 476–87.

Viets, H. R., 'The history of neurology in the last hundred years', *Bull. N.Y. Acad. Med.*, 1948, **24**, pp. 772–83.

Walshe, F. M. R., 'On the syndrome of the premotor cortex (Fulton) and the definition of the term premotor and motor with a consideration of Jackson's views on the cortical representation of movements', *Brain*, 1935, **58**, pp. 49–80.

Walshe, F. M. R., 'On the mode of representation of movements in the motor cortex with special reference to convulsions beginning involuntarily (Jackson), *Brain*, 1943, **66**, pp. 104–39.

Walshe, F. M. R., 'Queen Square: The cradle of British neurology', *Brit. Med. Bull.*, 1945, **3**, pp. 3–5.

Walshe, F. M. R., 'Thoughts upon the equation of mind with brain', *Brain*, 1953, 76, pp. 1–18.

Walshe, F. M. R., 'The nature and dimensions of nosography in modern medicine', *Lancet*, 1956, 2, pp. 1059–63.

Walshe, F. M. R., 'Some reflections upon the opening phase of the physiology of the cerebral cortex 1850–1900' in *The Brain and its Functions*, ed. F. N. L. Poynter, Oxford, 1958, pp. 223–4.

Walshe, F. M. R., Present and future of neurology', *Arch. Neurol.*, 1960, 2, pp. 83–8.

Walshe, F. M. R., 'Contributions of John Hughlings Jackson to neurology', *Arch. Neurol.*, 1961, 5, pp. 119–31.

Weschler, I. S., *A Textbook of Neurology*, Philadelphia and London, 1927.

Weschler, I. S., 'On the broadening concepts of neurology', *Neurol.*, 1956, 6, pp. 775–85.

Wetherill, J. H., 'The York Medical School', *Med. His.*, 1961, 5, pp. 253–69.

Whitty, C. W. M., and Lewin, W., 'Vivid day-dreaming following anterior cingulectomy', *Brain*, 1957, 80, pp. 72–6.

Whitty, C. W. M. and Lewin, W., 'A Korsakoff syndrome in the post-cingulectomy confusional state', *Brain*, 1960, 83, pp. 648–53.

Williams, D., 'The structure of emotions reflected in epileptic experiences', *Brain*, 1956, 79, pp. 29–67.

Williams, D., 'Old and new concepts of the basis of consciousness' in *The Brain and its Functions*, ed. F. N. L. Poynter, London, 1958.

Williams, D., 'The Psychiatry of the Epileptic', *Proc. Roy. Soc. Med.*, 1963, 56, pp. 707–11.

Wilson, G. R., *Clinical Studies in Vice and Insanity*, Edinburgh, 1899.

Wilson, S. A. Kinnier, 'The psychical components of temporal (uncinate) epilepsy' in *Modern Problems in Neurology*, London, 1928, pp. 51–75.

Wilson, S. A. Kinnier, 'The Hughlings Jackson Century', *Lancet*, 1935, 1, pp. 882–3.

Wilson, S. A. Kinnier, *Neurology*, ed. A. Ninnian Bruce, 2 vols., London, 1940.

Wing, J. K., ed., 'Clinical concepts of schizophrenia' in *Schizophrenia: Towards a New Synthesis*, London, 1978, pp. 1–30.

Wood, H. C., *A Treatise on Therapeutics, comprising materia medica and toxicology, with special reference to the application of the physiological action of drugs to clinical medicine*, Philadelphia, 1874.

Young, R. M., *Mind, Brain and Adaptation in the 19th Century*, Oxford, 1970, pp. 179–233.

Zilboorg, G., 'Development of the dynamic process in psychiatry' in *The Historical Development of Physiological Thought*, ed. Chandler McG. Brooks and Paul F. Cranefield, New York, 1959.

Index